Abbreviations Guide

An ABC for the construction industry

Abbreviations Guide

An ABC for the construction industry

Peter Adderley

RIBA Publications

© Peter Adderley 1990

Published by
RIBA Publications Ltd
Finsbury Mission, Moreland Street, London EC1V 8BB

ISBN 0 947877 39 8

Series editor: Alaine Hamilton

Book design by Penny Mills
Typeset by Goodfellow & Egan, Cambridge
Printed by Billing and Sons Ltd, Worcester

Other titles in the Professional Communication series:
Writing Matters by Alaine Hamilton
Computers Count by Jaki Howes
Writing Dissertations by Alaine Hamilton

Contents

Preface

Abbreviations exist in great profusion and variety, the inevitable result of trends and preoccupations in business, industry and the professions. They can bemuse and irritate, but we cannot do without them.

This book includes many of the abbreviations associated with professional practice in the construction industry, and a browse through its pages may also throw light down some unfamiliar byways. It is intended primarily as a reference document, but I hope it will provide enjoyment as well as enlightenment.

Peter Adderley
June 1990

Definitions

Abbreviation
A short expression for a longer word, phrase or concept. It can be formed by shortening words in various ways:

- stopping a word short (sub = subscription; ad = advertisement);
- giving the first and last letters only (wt = weight);
- using the initials of the main etymological elements (cg = centigram);
- using the first letter plus a selection of others to indicate the general sound (avdp = avoirdupois);
- merging two words into one ('portmanteau' words such as brunch, smog).

Alphabetism
An unpronounceable combination formed from the initial letters of words (JCT, BBC, RTZ).

Acronym
A pronounceable word formed from the initial letters of other words (Ernie, laser, Nato, Unesco).

'Irregular' pronunciations sometimes develop. Alphabetisms can be made pronounceable by the insertion of vowels. R M J M (formerly Robert Matthew Johnson-Marshall) is usually pronounced RUMJUM. Conversely, some acronyms are spelt out even though they are pronounceable, such as I C I.

Code
An artifically-determined abbreviation as part of a reference system. Codes may use letters (postcodes), figures (UDC classification), symbols (as on technical drawings) or electronic signals (in databases). Some are derived from the items they represent (AB = Aberdeen); others bear no relation to them (J = 'Waterproofing' in the Common Arrangement system).

Symbol
A mark or character taken as the conventional sign of some object or idea or process. It could be a single dot, perhaps the ultimate form of abbreviation. Symbols can have legal and other functions, as in logos, trade marks and road signs. A well-known example is the BSI kitemark.

Introduction

Abbreviations are age-old. Writing itself, in the form of cuneiform and hieroglyphics, developed from attempts to represent ideas and events graphically. The Romans used abbreviations for counting the years from the foundation of their city (AUC = *Anno urbis conditae*) and for expressing their conception of the State (SPQR = *Senatus populusque Romanus*). They conveyed their good wishes at the end of a letter with a simple SVBEEV (*Si vales, bene est, ego valeo*). One of the earliest abbreviations still used is INRI (*Iesus Nazarenus Rex Iudaeorum*).

In the twentieth century there has been an explosion of abbreviations, particularly acronyms, due to a large growth in bureaucracy — governmental, military and commercial. During the first world war, the Defence of the Realm Act 1914 became abbreviated to DORA. Many other acronyms were devised not only to serve as aids to memory but also to soften the harsh realities of war.

The second world war accelerated this growth. The American Army is credited with SNAFU (approximate translation: Situation Normal — All Fouled Up), while both the forces and the population at home were soon decorating their letters with SWALK (Sealed With A Loving Kiss), as well as messages of a rather more pressing nature, such as NORWICH.

In the 1960s the influence of computers began to be reflected in the language, and by the 1980s it had become infested with RAMs and ROMs and WYSIWYGs. Pressure groups have always vied with one another in devising eye-catching names, from the simple ASH (Action on Smoking and Health) to the tortuous VIOLENT (Viewers Intent On Listing Violent Episodes on Nationwide Television). We are now so acronym-conscious that we automatically scan the titles of organisations to see what the initials spell.

Some acronyms enter the language as ordinary words, their origins forgotten. The process is gradual: first the punctuation is omitted, and then the capital letters. Well-known examples are radar (radio detection and ranging) and laser (light amplification by the stimulated emission of radiation).

Abbreviations provide a useful shorthand; they are convenient, they save space, they save time, and they assist recognition and precision.

The ideal abbreviation is both apt and memorable. (This point does not seem to have been fully grasped by whoever came up with COMSUBCOMNELMCOMHEDSUPPACT for Commander, Subordinate Command, US Naval Forces Eastern Atlantic and Mediterranean, Commander Headquarters Support Activities.)

Mnemonics are abbreviations deliberatedly designed to be memory aids or teaching tools. Those struggling to remember the colours of the rainbow may find ROY G BIV more memorable than Red–Orange–Yellow–Green–Blue–Indigo–Violet.

Abbreviations, then, are remarkably varied in their origins, form and usage, and are an important part of our everyday language. As this guide demonstrates, the construction industry has more than its fair share of them.

About this Guide

Scope

The abbreviations gathered for this guide reflect a broad view of the construction industry and its place in the modern world. The prime purpose is to record and explain what occurs. For that reason some historic abbreviations are included, such as imperial units of measurement and superseded organisations, as these still occur widely and might need explanation.

Entries generally state only what an abbreviation stands for; the guide does not try to be a dictionary of meanings or a glossary of terms, although a little explanatory information is given in some cases.

The items included have been compiled from many sources: directories, other lists of abbreviations, textbooks and the press. Accuracy cannot be guaranteed, as it is impossible to check every item at source, or to spot every change as it happens. Inevitably many abbreviations will have been missed – some of them obscure, some blindingly obvious. The author would welcome the correction of errors, suggestions for additional items or subjects and comments on the display of items.

Arrangement

The guide is arranged in three parts. Part 1 is a straightforward A–Z list of abbreviations of all kinds. Part 2 contains classified lists of abbreviations which allow items and relationships in particular fields to be studied. Part 3 lists more detailed or specialised works giving further information about items listed in this guide, such as the functions and addresses of organisations and the meaning and use of scientific terms and units.

In Part 1 and in some of the lists in Part 2, entries are arranged in strict alphabetical order. If an abbreviation has more than one explanation, these too are in alphabetical order.

Numbers precede letters, including when they occur in the middle of abbreviations (eg H_2O comes before HAC). Punctuation and the difference between upper and lower case have been ignored in determining alphabetical order.

The following conventions have been adopted.

UPPER AND LOWER CASE

For consistency, acronyms of organisations are given in capital letters, even though some now usually use lower case (eg Nato). Capital initial letters are used for names and titles, and to indicate uniqueness (there are many 'housing associations', but only one 'Housing Corporation'). Elsewhere, lower case is used as much as possible.

NAMES OF COMPANIES AND ORGANISATIONS

'The', 'Ltd' and 'PLC' have been omitted unless they are incorporated in an acronym.

BRACKETS

Round brackets following some entries contain additional or explanatory information (eg an alternative name, a parent organisation, the subject area, perhaps the origin of an abbreviation).

ITALICS

Italic script is used for foreign words (other than organisations) and for publications.

LOED
 LOLN
FUNEX?
 SVFX
NFUNEM?
 OSVFM2
OKILFXNILFM
 SUFNRTTFMNX

L for bet

Although Jonathan Swift devised a prototype in the 1720s, the comic phonetic alphabet was largely developed during the 1920s and '30s, sparked off by signallers having fun during the first world war. This is just one selection from the many variations.

A for 'orses
B for mutton
C for yourself
D for dumb
E for brick
F for vest
G for police
H for retirement
I for got
J for oranges
K for cavern
L for fairy
M for size
N for lope
O for there
P for relief
Q for tickets
R for pint
S for you
T for chewing
U for mystic
V for l'amour
W for a quid
X for breakfast
Y for mistress
Z for a laugh

Part 1

Alphabetical lists

Numbers
A–Z lists

Numbers

1	tax return – partnership
1GL	1st generation language (computers: machine code – specific to machine)
2B–6B	black (pencil lead grades)
2D	2-dimensional (applied to CAD drafting systems)
2GL	2nd generation language (computers: assembler – specific to machine but extended capabilities)
2H–9H	hard (pencil lead grades)
2½D	"2½-dimensional" (applied to 2D CAD drafting systems which can generate elevations and certain 3D projections if heights are input; now obsolete)
3D	3-dimensional (applied to CAD modelling systems)
3F	light fittings by Marlin Lighting Ltd
3GL	3rd generation language (computers: written for variety of machines and then "compiled" for specific machine)
3i	Investment in Industry
3M	3M United Kingdom PLC (from Minnesota Mining and Manufacturing Co Ltd)
3 Rs	Reading, Riting and Rithmetic

4GL	4th generation language (computers: 3GL Mark 2)
11	tax return – self-employed
11P	tax return – higher-paid
11PA	claim for additional allowances
0345	local-call-rate telephone number
700	application form for 714
704	contractor's return to Inland Revenue listing payments made to subcontractors without deduction of tax
714	self-employed subcontractor's tax exemption certificate
715	exempt subcontractor's payment voucher
0800	free-call telephone number (freefone)
999	emergency telephone number
1992	completion date for creation of Single European Market (at midnight on 31 December)

A

A	ampere (unit of electric current – SI basic unit)
Å	Ångstrom (unit of length = 0.1 nm or 10^{-10} m)
A	answer
a	are (area of 100 m^2)
A	assembly drawing
a	atto (submultiple prefix: 10^{-18})
A	mass number (number of nucleons in a nucleus)
A	Preliminaries/General conditions (Common Arrangement)
A0	paper size: 841 × 1189 mm (basis of international A-series of trimmed paper sizes: a rectangle having an area of 1 m^2 and short and long sides in the proportion 1:$\sqrt{2}$)
A1	first-rate
A1	paper size: 594 × 841 mm (A0 ÷ 2)
A2	paper size: 420 × 594 mm (A0 ÷ 4)
A3	paper size: 297 × 420 mm (A0 ÷ 8)
A4	paper size: 210 × 297 mm (A0 ÷ 16)
A5	paper size: 148 × 210 mm (A0 ÷ 32)
A6	paper size: 105 × 148 mm (A0 ÷ 64)
A7	paper size: 74 × 105 mm (A0 ÷ 128)
A8	paper size: 52 × 74 mm (A0 ÷ 256)
A9	paper size: 37 × 52 mm (A0 ÷ 512)
A10	paper size: 26 × 37 mm (A0 ÷ 1024)
AA	Arboricultural Association
AA	*Architect's Appointment* (RIBA)
AA	Architects in Agriculture
AA	Architectural Association
AA	assisted areas (collective name for development areas and intermediate areas – DTI)
AAA	Amateur Athletic Association
AAA	Architectural Aluminium Association
AAA	triple A (top credit rating – USA)
AAAG	Amusement Arcade Action Group
AACPA	Autoclaved Aerated Concrete Products Association
AACR	Anglo-American cataloguing rules
AAD	appropriate alternative development
AADipl	Diploma in Architecture, Architectural Association
AAE	age and experience
AAE	American Association of Engineers
AAG	Architects in Agriculture Group
AAHB	Ayrshire and Arran Health Board
AAI	Architectural Association of Ireland
AAIS	Arboricultural Advisory and Information Service (Forestry Commission)
AAL	Association of Assistant Librarians
AAMA	Architectural Aluminium Manufacturers Association
AAP	architectural advisory panel
AASA	Architectural Association School of Architecture
AAU	Academy of Architecture of the USSR
AB	Aberdeen (postcode area)
AB	air brick
ab	as before
ABA	Association of British Archaeologists
ABACUS	Architecture and Building Aids Computer Unit Strathclyde
ABB	Architects and Building Branch (DES)
ABBF	Association of Bronze and Brass Founders
ABC	Abridged Building Classification for Architects, Builders and Civil Engineers (IBCC, 1955)
ABC	Allied Bar Coaters
ABC	the English alphabet
ABCA	Standards Bodies of America, Britain, Canada and Australia
ABC and D	*Architect Builder Contractor and Developer* (periodical)
ABCM	Association of Building Component Manufacturers
abd	as before described
ABHM	Association of Builders' Hardware Manufacturers
ABI	Associated Building Industries

ABI	Association of British Insurers
ab init	*ab initio* (Lat: from the beginning)
ABIOEC	see BRINDEX
ABO	area building officer
ABOI	Association of British Offshore Industries
ABP	see AB Ports
AB Ports	Associated British Ports
ABPP	Association of Black People and Planning
ABP Research	Associated British Ports Research Centre
ABPVM	Association of British Plywood and Veneer Manufacturers
ABR	acrylate-butadiene rubbers
ABRC	Advisory Board on Research Councils
ABRFM	Association of British Roofing Felt Manufacturers
ABS	acrylonitrile butadiene styrene copolymer
ABS	Architects Benevolent Society
ABSAM	Association of British Solid Fuel Appliance Manufacturers
ABSFAM	see ABSAM
ABT	Association of Building Technicians
ABTSA	Association of British Tree Surgeons and Arborists
a/c	account
ac	acre
Ac	actinium (chemical element)
ac	air conditioning
AC, ac	alternating current
Ac	altocumulus (cloud classification)
AC	*Appeal Cases* (law reports)
AC	Arts Council of Great Britain
ac	asbestos cement
AC	Audit Commission
ACA	Advisory Committee on Arbitration (Scottish Law Commission)
ACA	Aluminium Coatings Association
ACA	Architectural Claddings Association
ACA	Associate of the Institute of Chartered Accountants (England and Wales)
ACA	Association of Consultant Architects
ACAHEW	Advisory Committee for Agriculture and Horticulture in England and Wales
ACARD	Advisory Council for Applied Research and Development
ACAS	Advisory Conciliation and Arbitration Service
ACASLA	Association of Chief Architects of Scottish Local Authorities
ACAST	Advisory Committee on the Application of Science and Technology (UN)
ACB	Association of Certification Bodies
ACBA	Aggregate Concrete Block Association
acc	according
ACC	Association of Computer Clubs
ACC	Association of County Councils
ACCESS	Access Committee for England
ACCESS	automatic computer controlled electronic scanning system
ACCOMPLINE	on-line database: planning and local government subjects
ACDEPO	Association of Civil Defence and Emergency Planning Officers
ACE	Age Concern England
ACE	Architects Council of Europe
ACE	Association for the Conservation of Energy
ACE	Association of Consulting Engineers
ACE	Automatic Computing Engine (1950 computer)
ACEA	Association for Computing in Engineering and Architecture
ACEC	Advisory Council on Energy Conservation
ACGB	Arts Council of Great Britain (formerly CEMA)
ACHB	Argyll and Clyde Health Board
ACHCEW	Association of Community Health Councils of England and Wales
ACHO	Association of Chief Housing Officers
ACI	American Concrete Institute
ACIArb	Associate of the Chartered Institute of Arbitrators
ACIF	Agricultural Construction Industry Federation (FBIC)
ACM	copolymers of ethylacrylate or other acrylates and a small amount of a monomer which facilitates vulcanisation (rubbers)
ACMA	Asphalt and Coated Macadam Association
ACO	Association of Conservation Officers
ACoP	approved code of practice (HSC)

ACORD	Advisory Council in Research and Development
ACP	Africa, Caribbean and Pacific Ocean Countries (66 partners of the European Community by the Lomé Convention)
acph	air changes per hour
ACPHO	Association of County Public Health Officers
ACPM	Advisory Committee on Programme Management (EC)
ACPS	Advisory Council on Public Sanitation
ACR	annual confidential report
ACRDFP	Advisory Council on Research and Development for Fuel and Power (DEn)
ACRE	Action with Communities in Rural England
ACRE	automatic call recording equipment
ACS	Applied CAD Services (CAD dealer)
ACS	Association of Consulting Scientists
ACSAD	Arab Centre for the Study of Arid Zones and Dry Lands (LAS)
ACSHHPW	Advisory Committee on Safety and Health and Hygiene Protection at Work
ACSIR	Advisory Council for Scientific and Industrial Research
ACSTI	Advisory Committee for Scientific and Technical Information
ACT	advance corporation tax
ACTAC	Association of Community Technical Aid Centres
ACTO	Association of Chief Technical Officers
ACTS	Advisory Committee for Toxic Substances
ACTSS	Association of Clerical, Technical and Supervisory Staffs
ad	advertisement
A/D	analogue to digital (computers)
AD	*anno domini* (Lat: in the year of the Lord)
AD	approved document (building regulations)
AD	Architects' Directive (EC)
AD	*Architectural Design*
ad	as described
ADA	a programming language (computers)
ADA	Association of Drainage Authorities

ADAS	Agricultural Development and Advisory Service (MAFF)
ADB	African Development Bank
ADB	Asian Development Bank
ADC	advise dialling charge, advise duration and charge
ADC	Association of District Councils
ADC	automatic digital calculator
ADECO	dismantling workshop for organic and heavy water fuels (JRC – safety of nuclear materials)
ADF	average daily flow (sewage)
ADG	Architects Discussion Group
ad inf	*ad infinitum* (Lat: to infinity)
adj	adjust, adjustment
ADLO	Association of Direct Labour Organisations
admin	administration, administrator
ADP	automatic data processing
ADR	alternative dispute resolution (USA)
ADRLT(S)	Association of Directors of Recreation, Leisure and Tourism (Scotland)
ADSA	Automatic Door Suppliers Association
ad val	*ad valorem* (Lat: in proportion to the value)
A/E	architect or engineer (USA)
AEA	Aluminium Extruders Association
AEA	Atomic Energy Authority
AEC	architectural, engineering, constructional (CAD software)
AEC	Atomic Energy Commission
AECB	Association of Environment Conscious Builders
AECMA	Association Européenne des Constructeurs de Matériel Aerospatiel
AED	accident and emergency department (hospitals)
AEFT	Airfields Environment Federation Trust
AEI	Associated Electrical Industries
AENOR	Asociación Español de Normalización y Certificación (Spanish Standards Association)
AER	*All England Law Reports*
AERE	Atomic Energy Research Establishment (Harwell)
AES	Architecture and Engineering Series (IBM CAD system)
AESOP	Association of European Schools of Planning
AEU	Amalgamated Engineering Union

af, a/f	at fault
AF	audio frequency
AF	see Alfed
AFA	Access Flooring Association
AFC	Air Force Cross
AFESD	Arab Fund for Economic and Social Development
AFF	An Foras Forbatha (National Institute for Physical Planning and Construction – Ireland)
AFLA	Association of Fire Loss Adjusters
AFMU	terpolmer of tetrafluoroethylene-tri-fluoronitrosomethane and nitrosoperfluorobutyric acid (rubber)
AFNOR	Association Française de Normalisation (French Standards Association)
AfP	Atoms for Peace
AFRAeS	Associate Fellow of the Royal Aeronautical Society
AFTAAAC	Arab Fund for Technical Assistance to African and Arab Countries (LAS)
Ag	argentum (silver – chemical element)
AGC	Association of Gunite Contractors
AGE	area gas examiner
agg	aggregate
AGI	Association for Geographic Information
AGM	annual general meeting
AGONY	Architectural Guard of New York
AGR	advanced gas-cooled reactor
AGRIMED	Mediterranean Agriculture (agricultural research)
AHA	area health authority (NHS; now DHA)
AHIC	authorised home improvement centre
AHPWJC	Association of High Pressure Water Jetting Contractors
AHSS	Architectural Heritage Society of Scotland
AHY	Architectural Heritage Year (1975)
AI	architect's instruction
AI	artificial intelligence
AIA	American Institute of Architects
AIA	Associate of the Institute of Actuaries
AIArb	Associate of the Institute of Arbitrators
AIC	Architects in Industry and Commerce
AIC	Asbestos Information Centre
AICS	Association of Independent Computer Specialists
AID	Agency for International Development (USA)
AID	Area Improvement Design
AID	Arts in Danger
AIDO	Arab Industrial Development Organisation (LAS)
AIM	Advanced Informatics in Medicine in Europe
AIM	see ASLIB
AIM	European Association of Industries of Branded Products
AIMCAL	Association of Industrial Metallisers, Coaters and Laminators
AIN	area improvement note
AIOP	area improvement occasional paper
AIRO	Acoustical Investigation and Research Organisation
AIRTO	Association of Independent Research and Technology Organisations
AIS	aeronautical information service (airports)
AISS	Association Internationale de la Science du Sol (International Society of Soil Science)
AIUHWS	Association of Installers of Unvented Hot Water Systems (Scotland and Northern Ireland)
AIWP	Architectural Intake Working Party
AJ	*Architects' Journal*
AJA	Association of Jersey Architects
aka	also known as
Al	aluminium (chemical element)
AL	St Albans (postcode area)
ALA	Association of London Authorities (labour)
ALACA	Association of Local Authority Chief Architects
ALADI	Asociación Latino-Americana de Integración (= LAIA)
ALAM	Association of Lightweight Aggregate Manufacturers
ALANI	Association of Local Authorities of Northern Ireland
alara	as low as reasonably achievable

ALARM	All London Against the Road Menace	AMG	Asset Management Group (set up by BMI and DoI)
ALBA	Association of London Borough Architects	AMICE	Associate Member of the Institution of Civil Engineers
ALBES	Association of London Borough Engineers and Surveyors	AMIEE	Associate Member of the Institution of Electrical Engineers
ALBPO	Association of London Borough Planning Officers	AMIHVE	Associate Member of the Institute of Heating and Ventilating Engineers
ALC	Agricultural Land Commission		
ald	as last described	AMIMunE	Associate Member of the Institution of Municipal Engineers
ALECSO	Arab League Educational, Cultural and Scientific Organisation (LAS)	AMIStructE	Associate Member of the Institution of Structural Engineers
ALEEM	see ALEM		
ALEM	Association of Loading and Elevating Equipment Manufacturers	amp	ampere, amperage
		amp	amplifier
A-level	advanced level (GCE)	AMS	all main services
Alfed	Aluminium Federation	AMS	Ancient Monuments Society
ALGES	Association of Local Government Engineers and Surveyors	AMS	Association of Metal Sprayers
		AMU	Associated Mineworkers Union
ALGOL	algorithmic language (computers)		
ALHE	Association of London Housing Estates	ANC	Association for Neighbourhood Councils
ALI	Associate of the Landscape Institute	ANC	Association of Noise Consultants
		AND	a logic gate (computers)
ALJR	*Australian Law Journal Reports*	ANK	address not known
ALLC	Association of Larger Local Councils	ANM	copolymers of ethylacrylate or other acrylate and acrylonitrile (rubbers)
All ER	*All England Law Reports*		
All ER Rep	*All England Law Reports Reprint*	ANPO	Association of National Park Officers
ALR	Association of Lighting Retailers	ANS	advanced nursery stock (horticulture)
alt	alteration		
alt	alternate	ANSI	American National Standards Institute
alt	alternative		
ALU	arithmetic logic unit (computers)	ANT	Antrim, Northern Ireland (BS code)
		ANZUS	Australia New Zealand United States
Am	americium (chemical element)		
AM	amplitude modulation		
am	*ante meridiem* (Lat: before midday)	AOA	Association of Official Architects
AMA	Association of Metropolitan Authorities	AOB	any other business
		AODC	Association of Offshore Diving Contractors
AMASI	Associate Member of the Architects and Surveyors Institute	AOH	Applied Occupational Hygiene
AMC	Association of Municipal Corporations	AONB	area of outstanding natural beauty
		AOS	an operating system (computers)
AMDEA	Association of Manufacturers of Domestic Electric Appliances	AOSM	Arab Organisation for Standardisation and Metrology (LAS)
AMDUSSE	Association of Manufacturers of Domestic Unvented Supply Systems Equipment (MODUSSE)		
		AOTC	Associated Offices Technical Committee
AME	Association of Municipal Engineers		
AMEME	Association of Mining, Electrical and Mechanical Engineers	AP	Architectural Press
AMF	Arab Monetary Fund	APA	American Plywood Association

APA	Association of Public Analysts
A-party	originator of telephone call
APCC	Association of Professional Computer Consultants
APCG	Air Photo Cover Group (OS)
APD	*Authors' and Printers' Dictionary*
APDE	Association of Painters and Decorators Employers
APE	amalgamated power engineering
APE	automatic photomapping equipment
APEX	Association of Professional, Executive, Clerical and Computer Staffs
APFOLM	Association of Playing Fields Officers and Landscape Managers
APHI	Association of Public Health Inspectors
API	American Petroleum Institute
API	*Architectural Periodicals Index*
API	Association of Plastics Institutes
API	Association of Play Industries
APL	a programming language (computers)
APLE	Association of Public Lighting Engineers
APM	Association of Project Managers
APO	Air Photographs Officer (SDD)
APO	Association of Planning Officers
appd	approved
approx	approximately
appvd	approved
APR	annual percentage rate
Apr	April
apropos	to the purpose, with respect to (from French *àpropos*)
APRS	Association for the Protection of Rural Scotland
APSAS	Association of Public Service Administrative Staff
APSPE	Association of Public Service Professional Engineers
APT	advanced passenger train
Apt	apartment
APT	automatic public toilet
APTEM	Association of Passenger Transport Executives and Managers
AQUA EUROPA	European Federation for Water Treatment
AQUALINE	on-line database: water resources and supplies
AR	acrylic rubbers
AR	Arbitration Rules (JCT)
AR	*Architectural Review*
Ar	argon (chemical element)
ARA	Associate of the Royal Academy
ARC	Agricultural Research Council
ARCA	Asbestos Removal Contractors Association
ARCA	Associate of the Royal College of Art
arch	archaeology, archaeological, archaeologist
arch	architecture, architectural, architect
archt	architect
ARCONIS	Architecture and Construction Information Service
ARCS	Associate of the Royal College of Science
ARCUK	Architects Registration Council of the United Kingdom
ARD	Ards, Northern Ireland (BS code)
ARE	Arab Republic of Egypt
ARIBA	Associate of the Royal Institute of British Architects (pre-1971)
ARICS	Associate of the Royal Institution of Chartered Surveyors
ARM	Armagh, Northern Ireland (BS code)
ARM	Association of Recreation Managers
ARMS	Association of Roofing Materials Suppliers
ARQ	automatic request for re-send (telecommunications)
arr	arrival
ARR	average rate of return
ARSA	Associate of the Royal Scottish Academy
ARSH	Associate of the Royal Society of Health
ARSO	African Regional Organisation for Standardisation
art	article (of a government order or legal document)
art	artificial
artic	articulated vehicle
ARTSM	Association of Road Traffic Sign Makers
ARWA	Associate of the Royal West of England Academy
ARY	all risks yield
As	altostratus (cloud classification)
As	arsenic (chemical element)
ASA	Aberdeen Society of Architects (RIAS chapter)
ASA	Amateur Swimming Association

ASA	American Standards Association
ASAC	Asian Standards Advisory Committee
asap	as soon as possible
asb	asbestos
ASB	Association of Shell Boilermakers
ASBSBSW	Amalgamated Society of Boilermakers, Shipwrights, Blacksmiths and Structural Workers
ASC	Anglian Standing Conference (educational building consortium)
ASC	area of special control
ASCC	Automatic Sequence Controlled Calculator (1944)
ASCE	American Society of Civil Engineers
ASCE	Association of Sound and Communication Engineers
ASCHB	Association for Studies in the Conservation of Historic Buildings
ASCII	American Standard Code for Information Interchange
ASEAN	Association of South East Asian Nations
ASET	Association of Sculpture and Engineering Technologies
ASF	annual sinking fund
ASF	automatic sheet feeder (printing)
ASFPCM	Association of Structural Fire Protection Contractors and Manufacturers
ASHRAE	American Society of Heating, Refrigerating and Air-conditioning Engineers
ASHVE	American Society of Heating and Ventilation Engineers
ASI	Architects and Surveyors Institute
A-sizes	see A0, A1 etc; cf B-sizes and C-sizes
ASLC	Association of Street Lighting Contractors
ASLIB	Association for Information Management (formerly Association of Special Libraries and Information Bureaux; acronym retained)
ASME	American Society of Mechanical Engineers
ASME	Association of Small and Medium-sized Enterprises
ASMO	Arab Organisation for Standardisation and Metrology
ASN	area of special need

ASO	architect's site officer
ASP	Association of Self-employed People
asph	asphalt
ASR	alkali silica reaction
ASSILEC	Association of Dairy Industries of the EC
ASTM	American Society for Testing Materials
ASTM	ASTM sieve numbering system
ASTMS	Association of Scientific, Technical and Managerial Staffs (now merged with TASS as MSF)
ASW	Amalgamated Society of Woodworkers
ASW	Association of Scientific Workers
AT	Appropriate Technology
At	astatine (chemical element)
AT&T	American Telephone and Telegraph
ATC	air traffic control
ATC	*Annotated Tax Cases* (law reports)
ATDM	Association of Thermoplastic Domelight Manufacturers
ATIG	Alternative Technology Information Group
atm	standard atmosphere
ATT	Association of Tree Transplanters
att	attached, attachment
Au	aurum (gold – chemical element)
AU	polyester rubbers
AUAW	Amalgamated Union of Asphalt Workers
AUEW	Amalgamated Union of Engineering Workers
AUG	Acropolis User Group (computers)
Aug	August
AUG	Autocad User Group (computers)
auntie	automatic unit for national taxation and insurance
AUT	Association of University Teachers
AV	annual value
AV	audio-visual
av, ave	average
AVC	additional voluntary contribution (pensions)
Ave	Avenue
AVN	Avon (BS county code)
AW	Anglian Water

AWA	Aluminium Window Association	AWO	Association of Water Officers
AWARE	Association of Woodusers Against Rainforest Exploitation	AWOL	absent without leave, absent without official leave
AWG	American Wire Gauge		
AWO	area works officer (NHS)	axon	axonometric projection

B

b	bar (unit of pressure; abbreviation not recognised on its own, but used in mb for millibar and μb for microbar)	BADR	British Association for Disability and Rehabilitation
		BAE	Board of Architectural Education (ARCUK)
B	basement	BAFE	British Approvals for Fire Extinguishers
B	binary		
B	Birmingham (postcode area)	BAHPA	British Agricultural and Horticultural Plastics Association
B	black (pencil lead grade)		
B	boiler		
B	boron (chemical element)	BAIE	British Association of Industrial Editors
B	brick		
B	Complete buildings (Common Arrangement)	BAL	British Architectural Library (formerly RIBA Library)
		BAL	Building Adhesives Limited
BA	Bachelor of Arts	BALI	British Association of Landscape Industries
Ba	barium (chemical element)		
ba	bath	BALT	British Architectural Library Trust
BA	Bath (postcode area)	BAM	Bundesanstalt für Materialforschung und -prüfing (West Germany)
Ba	bathroom		
BA	British Airways		
BA	British Association System (screw thread designation system)	BAMA	British Aerosol Manufacturers Association
BA	Broads Authority	B and CE	building and civil engineering
BAA	Birmingham Architectural Association (RIBA branch)	B&CEHSM	Building and Civil Engineering Holidays Scheme Management
BAA	British Airports Authority (now BAA plc)	b&j	bed and joint
		b&p	bed and point
BAA	British Anodising Association	Bar	baroque
BAA	British Archaeological Association	BArch	Bachelor of Architecture
BABT	British Approvals Board for Telecommunications	BARMA	Boiler and Radiator Manufacturers Association
BACIRMCS	British Aggregate Construction Industry Ready-Mixed Concrete Scheme	BAS	British Acoustical Society
		BAS	British Antarctic Survey
		BAS	Building Advisory Service (BEC)
BACMI	British Aggregate Construction Materials Industries	BAS	building automation systems
		BASA	British Adhesives and Sealants Association
BACO	British Aluminium Company		
BACS	British Association for Chemical Specialities	BASEC	British Approvals Service for Electric Cables
BADEA	Banque Arabe pour le Développement Économique en Afrique	BASEEFA	British Approvals Service for Electrical Equipment in Flammable Atmospheres

BASIC	beginner's all-purpose symbolic instruction code (computers)
BAT	British Archaeological Trust (= Rescue)
baud	unit of data transmission speed: 1 baud = 2 bps (named after Baudot)
BB	Blackburn (postcode area)
BB	building bulletin (DES)
BB	double black (pencil lead grade)
BBA	British Board of Agrément (formerly Agrément Board)
BBB	treble black (pencil lead grade)
BBC	Britain in Bloom Campaign
BBC	British Bathroom Centre
BBC	British Bathroom Council
BBC	British Broadcasting Corporation
BBM	bolt bench mark (OS)
BBMA	British Bath Manufacturers Association
BBSA	British Blind and Shutter Association
BBT	Byways and Bridleways Trust
BC	before Christ
BC	borough council
BC	Bouwcentrum (Building Centre – Netherlands)
BC	British Coal
BC	British Columbia
BC	British Council
BC	Byggecentrum (Building Centre – Denmark)
BCA	Box Culvert Association
BCA	British Cement Association
BCAS	British Compressed Air Society
BCB	British Consultants Bureau
BCC	British Ceramic Confederation
BCC	British Coal Corporation
BCC	British Copyright Council
BCC	Business Co-operative Centre
BCCW	Building Control Consortium for Wales
BCD	binary coded decimal (computers)
BCDA	British Chemical Dampcourse Association
BCDC	Black Country Development Corporation
BCE	Board of Customs and Excise
BCEW	Boundary Commission for England and Wales
BCFA	British Contract Furnishing Association
BCG	Building Centre Group

BCGMA	British Commercial Glasshouses Manufacturers Association
BCIS	Building Cost Information Service (RICS)
BCLDI	British Clayware Land Drain Industry
BCMA	British Carpet Manufacturers Association
BCMA	British Colour Makers Association
BCMA	British Cubicle Manufacturers Association
BCMC	British Cable Makers Confederation
BCNI	Boundary Commission for Northern Ireland
BCPA	British Concrete Pumping Association
BCR	British Ceramic Research
BCRD	British Council for Rehabilitation of the Disabled
BCS	Black Country Society
BCS	Boundary Commission for Scotland
BCS	British Calibration Service (DTI)
BCS	British Computer Society
BCSA	British Constructional Steelwork Association
BCSC	British Council of Shopping Centres
BCSQACS	British Constructional Steelwork Quality Assurance Certification Scheme
BCT	Building Conservation Trust
BCTC	British Carpet Technical Centre
BCTC	British Ceramic Tile Council
BCURA	British Coal Utilisation Research Association
BCWG	British Curtain Wall Group (AWA)
b/d	barrels per day
BD	bill direct
bd	board
BD	Bradford, West Yorkshire (postcode area)
BD	*Building Design*
BDA	Brick Development Association
BDA	British Decorators Association
BDA	British Drilling Association
BDA	Bund Deutsche Architekten (West German Association of Architects)
BDC	Bristol Development Corporation
BDC	Business Design Centre
bdd	boarded
BDF	Bedfordshire (BS county code)

27

BDF	building distribution frame (telecommunications)
bdg	boarding
BDSA	Burnley District Society of Architects (part of RIBA Manchester branch)
BDWC	Bournemouth and District Water Company
Be	beryllium (chemical element)
BE	*Building Enquirer*
BEA	British Electricity Authority
BEAB	British Electrotechnical Approvals Board
BEAMA	Federation of British Electrotechnical and Allied Manufacturers Associations
BEB	Build Electric Bureau
BEC	Building Employers Confederation (formerly NFBTE)
BECA	British Exhibition Contractors Association
BEDA	British Electrical Development Association
BEDA	Bureau of European Designers Associations (EC)
BEE	Business Efficiency Exhibition
BEEC	Buildings Energy Efficiency Confederation
BEITA	Business Equipment and Information Technology Association
BEMA	British Electrical Manufacturers Association
BEMS	building energy management system
Benelux	Belgium, Netherlands and Luxembourg
BER	bit error rate (computers)
BES	Borough Engineers Society
BES	British Ecological Society
BES	Business Expansion Scheme
BESA	British Earth Sheltering Association
BESA	British Electrical Systems Association
BESA	British Engineering Standards Association
BESCA	Building Engineering Services Certification Authority
BET	Building Experiences Trust
BETA	Business Equipment Trade Association (now BEITA)
BETAB	see BEAB
BETI	Barlanark Employment and Training Initiative (Glasgow)

BEUC	European Bureau of Consumers Unions
BEWA	British Effluent and Water Association
b/f	brought forward
BFA	British Foundry Association
BFB	broad flanged beam
BFC	British Fabric Consultants
BFICC	British Facsimile Industry Consultative Committee
BFM	British Furniture Manufacturers Federation
BFMA	British Floorcovering Manufacturers Association
BFMF	see BFM
BFPSA	British Fire Protection Systems Association
BFRC	British Flat Roofing Council
BFS	Belfast, Northern Ireland (BS code)
BFSA	British Fire Services Association
BG	Birmingham Gauge (thickness of metal sheet)
BG	British Gas
BG	British Gypsum
BG	Builder Group
BGC	British Gas Corporation
BGC	British Gas Council
BGIRA	British Glass Industry Research Association
BGMF	British Glass Manufacturers Federation
BGS	British Geological Survey
BGS	British Geotechnical Society
BGT	Business Growth Training
BH	bottom-hung
BH	Bournemouth (postcode area)
BHAB	British Helicopter Advisory Board
BHB	Borders Health Board
bhp	brake horsepower
BHRA	British Hotels and Restaurants Association
BHRA	British Hydraulics Research Association
BHRCA	British Hotels Restaurants and Caterers Association
BI	Barbour Index
Bi	bismuth (chemical element)
bi	build in
BIAC	Business and Industry Advisory Committee (OECD)
BIAT	British Institute of Architectural Technicians (formerly SAAT)
BIC	Building Industry Convention

BIC	Building Industry Council (now CIC)
BICEPS	Bioformatics Collaborative European Programme and Strategy
BICS	British Institute of Cleaning Science
BIEC	British Invisible Exports Council
BIET	British Institute of Engineering Technology
BIF	British Industries Fair
BIFCA	British Industrial Furnace Constructors Association
BIFF	British Industrial Fasteners Federation
BIID	British Institute of Interior Design
BIIR	bromo-isobutene-isoprene (rubber)
BILC	*British International Law Cases*
BILG	Building Industry Libraries Group (renamed CIIG)
BIM	bit image mode (printing)
BIM	British Institute of Management
BINDT	see BInstNDT
BInstNDT	British Institute of Non-Destructive Testing
BIPM	International Bureau of Weights and Measures
BIR	Board of Inland Revenue
BIR	British Institute of Radiology
BIS	Bank for International Settlements
BISCC	see BRISCC
BISF	British Iron and Steel Federation
BISPA	British Independent Steel Producers Association
BISRA	British Iron and Steel Research Association
bit	binary digit
bit	bitumen
BIT	Building Industry Trust (RIBA)
BITS	BSI Information Technology Service
BJ	black japanned
bj	breaking joint
Bk	berkelium (chemical element)
bk	brick
BKM	Buckinghamshire (BS county code)
bkwk	brickwork
BL	Bolton (postcode area)
BL	British Library
BLA	Ballymena, Northern Ireland (BS code)

BLA	British Lift Association
BLAISE	British Library automated information service
BLD	Bachelor of Landscape Design
bldg	building
BLF	British Laminated Plastics Fabricators Association
BLLD	British Library, Lending Division
BLMA	British Ladder Manufacturers Association
BLMA	British Lead Manufacturers Association
BLMA	British Lock Manufacturers Association
BLPFA	see BLF
BLR	*Building Law Reports*
BLR	*Business Law Review*
BLY	Ballymoney, Northern Ireland (BS code)
BM	bench mark (OS)
BM	British Museum
BMA	bronze metal antique
BMCIS	Building Maintenance Cost Information Service
BMEF	British Mechanical Engineering Federation
BMEG	Building Materials Export Group
BMF	Builders Merchants Federation
BMHB	British Materials Handling Board
BMI	Building Maintenance Information (RICS)
BMIS	Building Materials Information Services
BMMG	British Microcomputer Manufacturers Group
BMP	National Council of Building Material Producers
BMPCA	British Metallurgical Plant Constructors Association
BMR	*Building Market Report*
BMS	building management system (computers)
bn	billion
BN	Brighton (postcode area)
BNB	Banbridge, Northern Ireland (BS code)
BNCOLD	British National Committee on Large Dams
BNEC	British Nuclear Energy Conference
BNES	British Nuclear Energy Society
BNF	British Nuclear Fuels
BNFMF	British Non-Ferrous Metals Federation
BNOC	British National Oil Corporation

BNR	Barlanark Neighbourhood Revitalisation Project (Glasgow)
BOC	British Oxygen Company
BOCE	Board of Customs and Excise
BOD	biochemical oxygen demand
BofT	Board of Trade
BOR	Borders Region, Scotland (BS code)
BOS	a computer operating system
BOSCA	British Oil Spill Control Association
BOT	Board of Trade
BOTB	British Overseas Trade Board
BP	Bat Project (Vincent Wildlife Trust)
bp	boiling point
BP	British Petroleum
BPA	British Parking Association
B-party	recipient of telephone call
BPB	British Plaster Board
BPCF	British Precast Concrete Federation
BPF	British Plastics Federation
BPF	British Ports Federation
BPF	British Property Federation
bpi	bits per inch (computers)
BPIC	Building Project Information Committee (successor to CCPI)
BPL, BPl	Bachelor of Planning
BPLG	British Parliamentary Lighting Group
BPMA	British Pump Manufacturers Association
BPN	building preservation notice
BPP	Best Practice Programme (EEO)
BPRU	Building Performance Research Unit (University of Strathclyde)
bps	bits per second (computers)
BPT	building preservation trust
BPWG	British Plastics Window Group
Bq	becquerel (unit of radioactivity)
BQA	British Quality Association
BQ(s)	bill(s) of quantities
BQSF	British Quarrying and Slag Federation
BR	bedroom
Br	British
BR	British Rail
Br	bromine (chemical element)
BR	Bromley (postcode area)
BR	building regulations
BR	butadiene rubber
BRA	British Resorts Association

BRAC	Building Regulations Advisory Committee
BRB	British Railways Board
BRC	Bituminous Roofing Council
BRCMA	see BRoCMA
BRD	*Building Regulations Decisions*
BRDC	British Research and Development Corporation
BRE	Building Research Establishment (DOE)
BRECSU	Building Research Energy Conservation Support Unit (BRE)
BREFAN	fan pressurisation rig for air leakage tests on buildings (BRE)
BREMA	British Radio and Electronic Equipment Manufacturers Association
BRERWULF	BRE real-time wind uniform load follower (test rig)
BRE(SL)	BRE (Scottish Laboratory)
BRETC	BRE Technical Consultancy
BRF	British Road Federation
BRIC	Biotechnology Regulations Inter-Service Communities (EC)
BRIDGE	Biotechnology Research for Industrial Development and Growth in Europe
BRINDEX	Association of British Independent Oil Exploration Companies
BRISCC	British Iron and Steel Consumers Council
Brit	British
BRITE	Basic Research in Industrial Technologies for Europe (EC)
BRK	Berkshire (BS county code)
brkts	brackets
BRMA	British Reinforcement Manufacturers Association
BRMA	British Resin Manufacturers Association
BRMA	British Rubber Manufacturers Association
BRMCA	British Ready Mixed Concrete Association
BRoCMA	Bitumen Roof Coating Manufacturers Association
BRR	book rate of return
brrs	bearers
brs	brass
BRS	British Road Services
BRS	Building Research Station (now part of BRE)
BRUFMA	British Rigid Urethane Foam Manufacturers Association
BS	Bachelor of Science

BS	bedspace
bs	both sides
BS	Bristol (postcode area)
BS	British standard
BSA	Berks Society of Architects (RIBA branch)
BSA	Birmingham School of Architecture
BSA	British Sign Association
BSA	Bucks Society of Architects (RIBA branch)
BSA	Building Societies Association
BSA	Byggeriets Studiearkiv (National Centre for Building Documentation – Denmark)
BSAP	Bartlett School of Architecture and Planning (University College London)
BSB	British standard beam
BSc	Bachelor of Science
BSC	binary synchronous communications, or bi-synch
BSC	British Safety Council
BSC	British standard channel
BSC	British Standard Cycle (screw thread designation scheme)
BSC	British Steel Corporation
BSCP	British standard code of practice
BS/D	bedspaces per dwelling
BSEA	British standard equal angle
BSF	British Stone Federation
BS/H	bedspaces per hectare
BSI	British Standards Institution
BSIA	British Security Industry Association
BSI QAS	BSI Quality Assurance Services
BSIRFS	BSI registered firms scheme of assessed capability
B-sizes	ISO series of trimmed paper sizes based on a size for B0 of $2^{\frac{1}{2}}$ m² (cf A-sizes and C-sizes)
bsm	both sides measured
BSMGP	British Society of Master Glass Painters
bsmt	basement
BSO	bank standing order
BSO	Business Statistics Office
BSRIA	Building Services Research and Information Association
BSRU	Building Services Research Unit (University of Glasgow)
BSS	British Standards Society
BSS	British standard specification
BSSM	British Society for Strain Measurement
BST	British standard tee
BST	British Summer Time
BSUA	British standard unequal angle
BSUB	British standard universal beam
BT	Belfast (postcode area)
BT	bidet
BT	British Telecommunications, British Telecom
BTA	British Tourist Authority
BTC	British Textile Confederation
BTC	British Transport Commission
BTCV	British Trust for Conservation Volunteers
BTDB	British Transport Docks Board
BTEC	Business and Technician Education Council
BTIA	British Tar Industry Association
btm	bottom
BTP	Bachelor of Town and Country Planning
BTR	Basic Technological Research
BTS	British Tunelling Society
BTU	British thermal unit
BUD	British Urban Development
BUDSU	British Urban Development Services Unit (DOE)
BUILD	building users' insurance against latent defects
BUTYL	butyl rubber
BV	besloten vennootschap (Du: private limited company)
BVT	Bourneville Village Trust
B/W, b/w	black and white
BWB	British Waterways Board
BWC	Bristol Water Company
BWEA	British Wind Energy Association
BWF	British Woodworking Federation
BWG	Birmingham Wire Gauge
BWIG	British Water Industries Group
bwk	brickwork
BWMA	British Woodwork Manufacturers Association
BWPA	British Wood Preserving Association
BWR	boiling water reactor
byte	a unit of, normally, eight bits (computers)
Byz	Byzantine
Bz	benzene
BZ	British Zonal (classification of light fittings by downward light spread)

31

C

C

C	100 (Roman numeral)	CAC	Cathedrals Advisory Commission for England
C	a high level computer language	CAC	Countryside Amenities Committee
C	carbon (chemical element)		
C	Celsius	CAC	Crafts Arts Council
C	centigrade	CACCI	Committee on the Application of Computers in the Construction Industry
c	centi (submultiple prefix: 10^{-3})		
C	centre line		
C	century	CACFOA	Chief and Assistant Chief Fire Officers Association
c	*circa* (Lat: about)		
C	cold (water)	CaCl$_2$	calcium chloride (accelerator for concrete)
C	component drawing		
C	cooker	CACM	Central American Common Market
C	coulomb (unit of electric charge)		
C	Demolition/Alteration/Renovation (Common Arrangement)	CaCO$_3$	calcium carbonate (chalk, limestone, marble etc)
		CACS	Clean Air Council for Scotland
C	see C-value	CAD	computer-aided design
c	velocity of light (= 2.997 × 10^8 m/s)	CADD	computer-aided design and drafting
		CADDIA	Co-operation in Automation for Data and Documentation for Import
C3	third-rate, physical weakling (lowest category in armed forces medical examination)		
		CAEU	Council of Arab Economic Unity
C$_3$A	tricalcium aluminate (constituent of cement)	CAG	Community Architecture Group (RIBA)
C4	envelope size: 229 × 324 mm; corresponding to A4 paper size	CAH	college of agriculture and horticulture
C5	envelope size: 162 × 229 mm; corresponding to A5 paper size	CAI	common air interface (telecommunications)
C6	envelope size: 114 × 162 mm: corresponding to A6 paper size	CAI	computer-assisted instruction
C7.5P, C10P etc		cal	calorie (unit of heat; superseded by joule)
	grades of concrete (BS 5328)		
		CAL	computer-assisted learning
CA	acetate, cellulose acetate	CALM	Campaign Against the Lorry Menace
CA	Cadmium Association		
Ca	calcium (chemical element)	CALUS	Centre for Advanced Land Use Studies
CA	Carlisle (postcode area)		
ca	cart away	CAM	Cambridgeshire (BS county code)
CA	conservation area		
CA	Court of Appeal	CAM	computer-aided manufacture
CAA	Cement Admixtures Association	CAMRASO	Cleaning and Maintenance Research and Service Organisation
CAA	Civil Aviation Authority		
CAA	Commonwealth Association of Architects		
		C and E	Customs and Excise
CAAD	computer-aided architectural design	c&f	cut and fit
		C and G	City and Guilds
CAB	butyrate, cellulose acetate butyrate	C&P	*Carrington and Payne* (law reports)
		CAP	cellulose acetate propionate
CABI	CAB International (formerly Commonwealth Agricultural Bureau)	c&p	cut and pin
		c&w	cutting and waste
		Cantab	Cantabrian (of Cambridge University)
CABIN	Campaign Against Building Industry Nationalisation		
		cantr	cantilever

CaO	calcium oxide (quicklime)
Ca(OH)$_2$	calcium hydroxide (slaked lime)
CAP	Common Agricultural Policy (EC)
CAP	community annoyance potential
CAPCIS	Corrosion and Protection Centre Industrial Services (UMIST)
CAPL	Coastal Anti-Pollution League
CAPT	Child Accident Prevention Trust
CAR	Cambridge Architectural Research
CAR	compound annual rate
CAR	computer-aided retrieval
CARC	Community Architecture Resource Centre (RIBA)
CARD	Campaign Against Racial Discrimination
CARE	Conservation Aid for Rainforests and Elephants
CARES	Certification Authority for Reinforcing Steels
CARICOM	Caribbean Community and Common Market
CARPA	Cathedral Area Residents Planning Association (Southwark)
CAS	Centre for Agricultural Strategy (University of Reading)
CAS	Clients' Advisory Service (RIBA)
CAS	Community Architecture (Scotland)
CASCO	ISO Committee on Conformity Assessment
CASE	Centre for Advanced Studies in Environment
CASE	computer-aided software engineering
CASEC	Confederation of Associations of Specialist Engineering Contractors
CaSO$_4$	calcium sulphate
CaSO$_4$.½H$_2$O	calcium sulphate hemihydrate (plaster of Paris)
CaSO$_4$.2H$_2$O	calcium sulphate dihydrate (gypsum)
CAT	Centre for Alternative Technology
CAT	city action team
CAT	college of advanced technology
CAT	college of art and technology
cath	cathedral
CATU	Ceramic and Allied Trades Union
CATV	cable television
cav	cavity
CAWS	Common Arrangement of Work Sections
CAZ	central activities zone
CB	Cambridge (postcode area)
cb	common brickwork
CB	Companion of the Bath
CB	conciliation board
C/B	cooker boiler
CB	county borough
Cb	cumulonimbus (cloud classification)
CBA	Council for British Archaeology
CBAE	Commonwealth Board of Architectural Education
CBC	county borough council
CBCC	Central Building Control Consortium
CBCSM	Council of British Ceramic Sanitaryware Manufacturers
CBD	central business district
CBDC	Cardiff Bay Development Corporation
CBE	Commander of the British Empire
CBI	Confederation of British Industry
CBIC	Building Information Centre, Coventry
CBL	computer-based learning
CBM	Commodore Business Machines
CBM	cut bench mark (OS)
CBMA	Concrete Brick Manufacturers Association
CBPA	Concrete Block Paving Association (Interpave)
CBR	Campaign for Bedsit Rights
CBR	Community Bureau of References (EC)
CBRPT	Confederation of British Road Passenger Transport
CBSS	Chief Building Surveyors Society
CBT	computer-based training
c/c	centre to centre
CC	chemical closet
Cc	cirrocumulus (cloud classification)
CC	city council
CC	Commons Commissioners
cc	copies
CC	Countryside Commission
CC	county council
CC	Crafts Council
CC	Crime Concern
cc	cubic centimetre
CCA	Cement and Concrete Association (now BCA)
CCA	copper chromium arsenic (timber preservative)
CCA	County Councils Association
CCAAP	Central Committee for the Architectural Advisory Panels

CCAHE	Convention for the Conservation of the Architectural Heritage of Europe (Council of Europe)
CCASG	Co-operation Council for the Arab States of the Gulf (usually known as GCC)
CCC	Central Criminal Court
CCC	Chaos Computer Club (Hamburg-based hackers)
CCC	Committee of Cultural Consultants (EC)
CCC	Community Consumer Council (EC)
CCC	Consumers Consultative Committee (EC)
CCC	Council for Cultural Co-operation (Council of Europe)
CCC	Council for the Care of Churches
CCC	Management Co-ordination Consultative Committee (EC)
CCCR	Central Committee on Commons Registration
CCD	charge coupled device
CCE	Church Commissioners for England
CCE	Commission of the European Communities
CCEWNH	Convention on the Conservation of European Wildlife and Natural Habitats (Council of Europe)
CCHPG	Centre for the Conservation of Historic Parks and Gardens (IAAS)
CCI	Centre de Creation Industrielle (Pompidou Centre, Paris)
CCIR	Comité Consultatif International de Radio (ITU)
CCITT	Comité Consultatif International des Telegraphes et Telephones (International Telegraph and Telephone Consultative Committee) (ITU)
CCL	Caribbean Congress of Labour
CCL	common command language (computers)
CCMA	Contract Cleaning and Maintenance Association
CCMI	Centre for Construction Market Information
ccn	close copper nailing
CCP	console command processor (computers)
CCPI	Co-ordinating Committee for Project Information (superseded by BPIC)
CCP/M	a control program (multi-tasking version of CP/M) (computers)
CCPR	Central Council for Physical Recreation
CCPR	Centre for Climate Prediction and Research (MO)
CCR	commitment concurrency and recovery (computers)
CCRO	community charge registration officer
CCRP	Central Council for Rivers Protection
CCRST	Comité Consultatif de la Recherche Scientifique et Technique (Consultative Committee for Scientific and Technical Research)
ccs	centres
CCS	Confederation of Construction Specialists
CCS	Countryside Commission for Scotland
CCSU	Council of Civil Service Unions
CCT	compulsory competitive tendering
CCT/CET	Common Customs Tariff/Common External Tariff (EC)
CCTV	closed circuit television
CCU	Civil Contingency Unit (Cabinet Office)
CCU	community charge unit
CCU	consumer control unit
CCUSBS	Committee for the Co-ordination of Underground Services on Building Sites
Cd	cadmium (chemical element)
cd	candela (unit of luminous intensity – SI basic unit)
CD	compact disc
CD	Compliance Directive (EC)
CD	contractor's design
CD 81	Standard Form of Building Contract with Contractor's Design 1981 (JCT)
CDA	comprehensive development area
CDA	Contract Design Association
CDA	co-operative development agency
CDA	Copper Development Association
CDC	Cumbernauld Development Corporation
CDCW	Cymdeithas Diogelu Cymru Wledig (Council for the Protection of Rural Wales)
CD-E	compact disc – erasable
CDEP	Central Directorate on Environmental Pollution (DOE)
CDP	Committee for Development Planning (UN: ECOSOC)

CDP	contractor's designed portion
CDP	Contractor's Designed Portion (supplement to JCT 80)
CD-R	compact disc – recordable
CD-ROM	compact disc – read only memory
CDRS	Construction Data Research Services
CDT	craft design technology
CDUNRSE	Committee on the Development and Utilisation of New and Renewable Sources of Energy (UN)
CDV	compact disc video
"CE"	see CE mark
Ce	cerium (chemical element)
CE	Church of England
CE	civil engineer
CE	clearing eye
CE	Communauté Européenne (European Community)
CE	Conseil de l'Entente (four West African states)
CE	Council of Europe
CEA	Central Electricity Authority
CEA	Conseil Européen des Architectes (presidents council)
CEAO	Communauté Économique de l'Afrique de l'Ouest
CEB	Central Electricity Board
CEBI	Centre for European Business Information
CEBM	Confederation of European Bath Manufacturers
CEC	Commission of the European Communities
CEC	Commonwealth Engineers Council
CEC	Crown Estate Commissioners
CECC	CENELEC Electronic Components Committee
CECED	European Committee of Manufacturers of Domestic Electrical Equipment (EC)
CECOP	European Committee of Workers Co-operative Productive Societies
CEDEFOP	European Centre for the Development of Vocational Training
CEE	Council for Environmental Education
CEE	International Commission on Rules for the Approval of Electrical Equipment
CEEC	Construction Economics European Committee; or European Committee of Construction Economists
CEEC	Council for European Economic Co-operation
CEEFAX	see facts (BBC TV information system)
CEEP	European Centre of Public Enterprises
CEFIC	European Council of Chemical Industry Federations
CEG	City Engineers Group
CEGB	Central Electricity Generating Board (superseded by NP and PG)
CEH	Centre on Environment for the Handicapped
CEI	Centre for Environmental Interpretation
CEI	Council of Engineering Institutions
CEL	Civil Engineering Laboratory (BRE)
cem	cement
CEM	College of Estate Management
cem	contract energy management
CEMA	Council for the Encouragement of Music and the Arts (now ACGB)
CEMAGB	Catering Equipment Manufacturers Association of Great Britain
CE mark	mark ("CE", for "Communauté Européenne") signifying that a product complies with the relevant requirements
CEMBUREAU	European Cement Association
CEMR	Council for European Municipalities and Regions
CEN	Central Region, Scotland (BS code)
CEN	European Committee for Standardisation
CEN/CENELEC	Joint European Standards Institution
CEng	Chartered Engineer
CENCER	CEN's certification body
CENELEC	European Committee for Electrotechnical Standardisation (electrotechnical counterpart of CEN)
CEOC	Colloque Européen des Organisations de Contrôle
CEP	community enterprise programme (now CP)
CEPOS	County Emergency Planning Officers Society
CEPT	Conference Européenne des Administrations des Postes et Telecoms (European Posts and Telecommunications Conference)

CER	Community Energy Research
CERA	Civil Engineering Research Association
Ceram Research	
	British Ceramic Research
CERD	Committee for European Research and Development
CERF	Council of Europe Resettlement Fund
CERI	Centre for Educational Research and Innovation (EC)
CERL	Central Electricity Research Laboratories
CERN	Conseil Européen de Recherche Nucléaire (European Organisation for Nuclear Research)
CERP	European Federation of Public Relations
CERTICO	ISO Committee on Certification
CES	Centre for Environmental Studies
CES	Centro Edile SpA (Building Centre – Italy)
CES	community enterprise scheme
CESPA	Campaign for Equal State Pension Ages
CET	Central European Time
CET	Common External Tariff (EC)
Cf	californium (chemical element)
CF	Cardiff (postcode area)
c/f	carry forward
cf	*confer* (Lat: compare)
CFA	Campaign for Architecture
CFA	Communauté Financière Africaine
CFA	Construction Fixings Association
CFA	Contract Flooring Association
CFA	Co-opération Financière en Afrique Centrale
CFB	Cavity Foam Bureau
CFBAC	Central Fire Brigades Advisory Council (England and Wales)
CFC	chlorofluorocarbon
cfi	cost, freight, insurance
CFI	Court of First Instance (EC)
CFIBC	see COFI
CFLP	Central Fire Liaison Panel
CFM	polychlorotrifluoroethylene (rubber) (same as PCTFE)
cfm	cubic feet per minute
CFP	Common Fisheries Policy (EC)
CFP	Communauté Française du Pacifique
CFP	Comptoirs Français du Pacifique
CFR	commercial fast reactor
cfs	cubic feet per second
cft	cubic feet

CFTC	Commonwealth Fund for Technical Co-operation
cg	centigram
CG	city grant (DOE)
CGA	colour graphics adaptor (computers)
CGBR	central government borrowing requirement
CGC	Management and Co-ordination Advisory Committee (EC)
CGE	Chief Gas Examiner (DEn)
CGI	computer graphics interface
CGM	computer graphics metafile
CGM	Conspicuous Gallantry Medal
CGPM	Conférence Générale des Poids et Mesures (General Conference on Weights and Measures)
CGS	centimetre gram second (system of units)
CGT	capital gains tax
CGV	Craigavon, Northern Ireland (BS code)
CH	central heating
Ch	*Chancery Reports* (law reports)
CH	Chester (postcode area)
ch	church
CH	college of horticulture
CH	Companion of Honour
CH$_4$	methane (marsh gas)
chal	channel
chap	chapel
chap	chapter
CHAPS	Clearing House Automated Payment System
CHAS	Catholic Housing Aid Society
CHCL	Campaign for Homes in Central London
ChD	*Chancery Division* (law reports)
CHDG	County Hall Development Group (London)
CHE	college of higher education
CHiCL	Campaign for Homes in Central London
CHP	combined heat and power
CHPA	Combined Heat and Power Association
CHPDH	combined heat and power district heating
CHR	Centre for Housing Research (Glasgow University)
CHS	Cheshire (BS county code)
CHS	circular hollow section
CHS	Commission on Human Settlements (UN: ECOSOC)

CHSG	Construction Health and Safety Group	CIE	Centro Italiano dell'Edilivia (Italian Building Station)
CI	cast iron	CIE	Commission Internationale de l'Eclairage (International Commission for Illumination - ICI)
CI	Channel Islands		
Ci	cirrus (cloud classification)		
CI	Commonwealth Institute	Cie	compagnie (Fr: company)
CI	Community Industry	CIEC	Cambridge Interdisciplinary Environmental Centre
Ci	curie (unit of activity of a radioactive substance)	CIEE	Conference of the Institution of Electrical Engineers
CIA	Chemical Industries Association	cif	cost, insurance, freight
CIAG	Construction Industry Advisory Group	CII	Construction Industry Institute (USA)
CIAM	Congrés Internationaux d'Architecture Moderne	CIIG	Construction Industry Information Group (formerly BILG)
CIArb	Chartered Institute of Arbitrators		
CIB	Conseil International du Batiment pour la Recherche l'Etude et la Documentation (International Research Council for Building Research Studies and Documentation)	CIIR	chloro-isobutene-isoprene (rubber)
		CIL	Computers in Libraries (annual exhibition and conference; formerly SCIL)
CIB	Corporation of Insurance Brokers	CILE	call information logging equipment
CIB	see CIOB		
CIBD	International Council for Building Documentation (now CIB)	CILL	*Construction Industry Law Letter*
		CILSS	Inter-state Committee for Drought Control in the SAHEL (African countries)
CIBS	Chartered Institution of Building Services (now CIBSE)		
CIBSE	Chartered Institution of Building Services Engineers	CIM	Chartered Institute of Marketing (charter 1989)
CIC	Construction Industry Council (formerly BIC)	CIM	*CI/SfB Construction Indexing Manual*
		CIMT	see CIMTECH
CICA	Construction Industry Computing Association	CIMTECH	National Centre for Information, Media and Technology
CICC	Construction Industry Conference Centre	CINET	International Network for Construction Market Information
CICE	Construction Industry Computer Exhibition (RIBAS)	CIOB	Chartered Institute of Building (formerly IOB)
CICI	Confederation of Information Communication Industries	CIP	commercially important passenger
CICI	*Current Information in the Construction Industry* (PSA)	CIPM	Commission International des Poids et Mesures (International Committee of Weights and Measures)
CICRIS	Co-operative Industrial Commercial Reference and Information Service		
CICS	Ceramic Industry Certification Scheme	circ	circle, circular (shape)
		circ	circular (document)
CICUG	Construction Industry Computer User Group	circ	circulation
		circ	circumference
CID	Centre for Industrial Development (Lomé Convention)	CIRIA	Construction Industry Research and Information Association
CID	Construction Industry Directorate (DOE)	CIS	central information services
		CI/SfB	Construction Indexing/SfB (UK version of SfB classification)
CID	Council of Industrial Design	CISPR	International Special Committee on Radio Interference
CIDST	Committee for Information Documentation Science and Technology (EC)	CISS	*Construction Industry Software Selector* (RIBAS)

CIT	Chartered Institute of Transport
CIT	*Construction Industry Thesaurus*
CITB	Construction Industry Training Board
CITES	Convention on International Trade in Endangered Species
CJ	Chief Justice
CJ	*Contract Journal*
ckd	checked
CKF	Carrickfergus, Northern Ireland (BS code)
CKT	Cookstown, Northern Ireland (BS code)
CL	ceiling limit (maximum permitted concentration of constituents of air)
CL	centre line
Cl	chlorine (chemical element)
cl	clause
CL	cover level (manhole)
CLA	Country Landowners Association
CLA	see CLASS
CLAE	Commission for Local Administration in England
CLAEU	Comité de Liaison des Architectes de l'Europe Unie (Liaison Committee for the Architects of a United Europe)
CLAIMS	Contract Law Advisory and Information Management System (database)
CLAS	Chartered Land Agents Society
CLAS	Commission for Local Administration in Scotland
CLASP	Consortium of Local Authorities Special Programme
CLASS	Concrete Lintel Association
CLAVA	County Land Agents and Valuers Association
CLAW	Commission for Local Administration in Wales
CLAW	Consortium of Local Authorities in Wales
CLAWSA	Cities of London and Westminster Society of Architects (RIBA branch)
CLCA	Concrete Lighting Column Association
CLD	*Construction Law Digest*
CLEAR	Campaign/Council for Lead-free Air
CLES	Centre for Land Economic Strategies
clg	ceiling

CLOA	Chief Leisure Officers Association
CLR	Coleraine, Northern Ireland (BS code)
CLT	computer language translator
CLV	Cleveland (BS county code)
CLY	*Current Law Yearbook*
cm	centimetre
CM	Chelmsford (postcode area)
CM	chloropolyethylene (rubber)
Cm	curium (chemical element)
CMA	contract management adjudication
CMA	Cumbria (BS county code)
CMB	Consortium of Method Building (METHOD)
CMC	caractère magnétique code (magnetic character code - computers)
Cmd	command paper
CMDC	Central Manchester Development Corporation
CMEA	Council for Mutual Economic Assistance (aka COMECON)
CMF	Cement Makers Federation
CMG	Conduct Monitoring Group (ARCUK)
CMI	computer-managed instruction
CML	computer-managed learning
CMLR	*Common Market Law Reports*
CMN	common market nation/national
CMOS	complementary MOS (computers)
CMPE	Contractors' Mechanical Plant Engineer
CMQAS	Cement Makers Quality Assurance Scheme
CMR	cellular mobile radio
CMRST	Committee on Manpower Resources for Science and Technology
CN	celluloid, nitrate, cellulose nitrate
CN	Council for Nature
CNAA	Council for National Academic Awards
CNIG	Construction National Interest Group
CNL	corrected noise level
CNMB	Central Nuclear Measurement Bureau (Euratom)
CNR	Committee on Natural Resources (UN: ECOSOC)
CNR	Consiglio Nazionale delle Ricerche (National Research Centre – Italy)
CNT	Commission for the New Towns

CO	Cabinet Office
CO	carbon monoxide
c/o	care of
CO	certificate of occupancy
Co	cobalt (chemical element)
CO	Colchester (postcode area)
Co	company
co	consisting of
CO	co-ordinating size
CO	polychloromethyloxiran, epichlorohydrin elastomer (rubber)
CO_2	carbon dioxide
coax	coaxial cable
COBOL	common business orientated language (computers)
Cobuild	Collins-Birmingham University international language database
COCOM	Co-ordinating Committee on Multilateral Export Controls
COD	cash on delivery
COD	*Concise Oxford Dictionary*
CODASYL	Conference on Data Systems Languages (USA)
codec	coder decoder
CODEST	European Development Committee for Science and Technology
CODEX	Codex Alimentarius Commission (UN)
CoEnCo	Council for Environmental Conservation
COFACE	Committee of Family Organisations in the EC
C of C	chamber of commerce
C of E	Church of England
C of E	Council of Europe
C of I	Church of Ireland
COFI	Council of Forest Industries of British Columbia
C of S	Church of Scotland
COGECA	General Committee for Agricultural Co-operation in the EC
COHSE	Confederation of Health Service Employees
COI	Central Office of Information
COID	Council of Industrial Design
COID	Council on International Development
col	colour, coloured
col	column
COL	computer-oriented language
COL	cost of living
Colombo Plan	
	Colombo Plan for Co-operative Economic and Social

	Development in Asia and the Pacific
COM	Commission of the EC proposals for legislation – the abbreviation marking Commission documents
COM	computer output on microfilm
COMAC	concerted action committee (EC)
COMAL	a high level programming language (computers)
COMECON	Council for Mutal Economic Assistance (aka CMEA)
COMETEC-GAZ	
	Economic Research Committee of the Gas Industry (EC)
COMETT	Community Action Programme in Education and Training for Technology (EC)
COMITEXTIL	Co-ordination Committee for the Textile Industries of the EC
comp	complete
COMP	Council of Management and Professional Staffs (TUC)
comp'n	completion
COMTECHSA	Community Technical Services Agency (Liverpool)
con	*contra* (Lat: against)
CON	Cornwall (BS county code)
conc	concrete
conf	conference
confed	confederation
CONIAC	Construction Industry Advisory Committee (HSC)
Con LR	*Construction Law Reports*
CON-NIG	Construction National Industry Group (HSE)
c on p	circular on plan
CONSTRADO	Constructional Steel Research and Development Organisation (now SCI)
cont	continued
conv	convector
co-op	co-operative
COPA	Commission of Agricultural Organisations in the European Community
COPANT	Pan American Standards Commission
COPCO	ISO council committee on consumer policy
copp	copper
CORAD	Committee on Restrictions Against the Disabled
CORAL	a high level programming language (computers)
CORDI	Advisory Committee on Industrial Research and Development (EC)

COREPER	Committee of Permanent Representatives (EC)
Corgi	Confederation for the Registration of Gas Installers
Corp	corporation
corr	corrugated
cos	cosine
cosec	cosecant
COSFPS	Commons, Open Spaces and Footpaths Preservation Society (now OSS)
COSHH	control of substances hazardous to health
CoSIRA	Council for Small Industries in Rural Areas (now RDC)
COSLA	Convention of Scottish Local Authorities
COST	Committee on European Co-operation in the field of Scientific and Technical Research
cot	cotangent
COT	Council on Tribunals
CoW	clerk of works
CP	car park
cP	centipoise (unit of dynamic viscosity)
CP	chromium-plated
CP	code of practice (BSI et al)
CP	code of procedure (NJCC et al)
CP	community programme
cp	compare
CPA	Chipboard Promotion Association
CPA	city partnership area
CPA	Concrete Pipe Association
CPA	Construction Plant-hire Association (originally the Contractors' Plant Association)
CPA	critical path analysis
CPC	circuit protective conductor
CPC	Code of Professional Conduct (RIBA)
CPC	Code Policy Committee (RIBA)
CPC	Community Patent Conventions (EC)
CPC	Crime Prevention Centre (Home Office)
CPD	Construction Products Directive (EC)
CPD	continuing professional development
cpd	cupboard
CPDA	Clay Pipe Development Association
CPDC	continuing professional development in construction professions
CPDC	CPD in Construction Group

CPETA	Computer and Peripherals Equipment Trade Association
CPF	Community Projects Fund (RIBA)
CPG	Consumer Protection Group (EC)
cpg	coping
CPI	Chief Planning Inspector
CPI	consumer price index
CPI	co-ordinated project information
CPM	cards per minute (data processing)
CP/M	control program for microcomputer; or control, program, monitor
CPM	critical path method
CPO	compulsory purchase order
CPO	county planning officer
CPOS	County Planning Officers Society
CPP	Consumer Protection Programme (EC)
CPPS	county planning policy statement
cpr	copper
CPRE	Council for the Protection of Rural England
CPRR	Council for the Preservation of Rural Romania
CPRW	Council for the Protection of Rural Wales (CDCW)
cps	characters per second
CPS	Commons, Open Spaces and Footpaths Preservation Society (now OSS)
cps	cycles per second (see also c/s)
CPSA	Civil and Public Services Association
CPU	central processing unit (computers)
CPVC	post-chlorinated PVC
CPVR	Campaign for the Protection of Villages in Romania
CR	chloroprene rubber, neoprene
Cr	chromium (chemical element)
CR	Construction References (PSA)
CR	Croydon (postcode area)
CRA	Concrete Repair Association
CRAC	Careers Research and Advisory Centre
CRAP	Central Register of Air Photography (for Scotland; Scottish Development Department)
CRAPE	Central Register of Air Photography for England (OS)
CRAPW	Central Register of Air Photography for Wales (Welsh Office)
crc	camera-ready copy

CRE	Coal Research Establishment (NCB)	csg	casing
Cres	Crescent	CSG	clear sheet glass
CREST	Committee on Scientific and Technical Research (EC)	CSI	Construction Surveyors Institute (now merged with FAS as ASI)
CRGI	see Corgi	CSIR	Commonwealth Council for Scientific and Industrial Research (now CSIRO)
CRM	Committee for Medical and Public Health Research (EC)		
CRM Society	Charles Rennie Mackintosh Society	CSIRA	see CoSIRA
		CSIRO	Commonwealth Scientific and Industrial Research Organisation
CRO	Companies Registration Office		
CRONOS/EUROSTAT		CSITC	Computing Services Industry Training Council
	European Community's Statistical Data Bank	C-sizes	ISO series of trimmed paper sizes based on a size for C0 of $2^{\frac{1}{4}}$ m^2 (cf A-sizes and B-sizes). Sizes also used for envelopes corresponding to A-sizes for trimmed paper (see C4 etc)
CRPB	Clyde River Purification Board		
CRRAG	Countryside Recreation Research Advisory Group		
CRS	cold-rolled steel		
crs	course		
CRSA	Cold Rolled Sections Association	CSLA	see COSLA
CRT	cathode-ray tube	CSM	Camborne School of Mines
CRTC	Clay Roofing Tile Council	CSM	chlorosulphonylpolyethylene, 'Hypalon' (rubber)
CRWC	Central Rights of Way Committee		
		csnk	countersunk
		CSO	Central Statistical Office
Cs	caesium (chemical element)	CSP	Convention on Soil Protection (Council of Europe)
CS	casein		
Cs	cirrostratus (cloud classification)	CSR	Castlereagh, Northern Ireland (BS code)
CS	Citizens' Support		
CS	Concrete Society	CSS	County Surveyors Society
CS	Conservation Society	CSSC	Centre for Strategic Studies in Construction (Reading University)
CS	crown silvered (electric light bulb)		
c/s	cycles per second (unit of frequency, superseded by hertz)	cSt	centistokes (unit of kinematic viscosity)
		CST	college of science and technology
CSA	Camden Society of Architects (RIBA branch)	CST	Euratom Scientific and Technical Committee
CSA	Canadian Standards Association		
CSA	Central Services Agency for Northern Ireland (Health)	CSTB	Centre Scientifique et Technique du Batiment (Scientific and Technical Building Centre - France)
CSA	Cheshire Society of Architects (RIBA branch)		
CSA	Computing Services Association	CSTC	Centre Scientifique et Technique de la Construction (Building Research Centre – France)
CSA	contract sum analysis		
CSA	Coventry Society of Architects (RIBA branch)		
		CSU	Civil Service Union
csa	cross-sectional area	CSW	Chartered Surveyor Weekly
CSAS	Construction Security Advisory Service (BEC)	CSWDB	Central Scotland Water Development Board
CSASHS	Common Services Agency for the Scottish Health Service		
		CT	Canterbury, Kent (postcode area)
CSBA	Calcium Silicate Brick Association	ct	cement
CSCU	consumer's supply control unit	CT	Civic Trust
CSDN	circuit switched data network	ct	coat
CSERB	Computer Systems and Electronic Requirements Board	CT	college of technology
		CT	Conservation Trust
CSEU	Confederation of Shipbuilding and Engineering Unions	CT	cordless telephone
		CT	Council on Tribunals

Ct	court
CT2	cordless telephone second generation
CTA	Channel Tunnel Association
CTA	triacetate, cellulose triacetate
CTC	city technology college
CTCC	Central Transport Consultative Committee
ctd	coated
CTEB	Council of Technical Examining Bodies
ctg	cutting
CTR	controlled thermonuclear research
CTRU	Civic Trust Regeneration Unit
CTSO	county trading standards officer
CTT	capital transfer tax (1975-86; superseded by IHT)
CTU	Central Technical Unit (ex-GLC architects, now privatised as CTU Ltd)
CU	consumer unit (electrical intake)
cu	cubic
Cu	cumulus (cloud classification)
Cu	cuprum (copper – chemical element)
CUA	Computer Users Association
CUBE	Concertation Unit for Biotechnology (secretariat to BRIC)
CUC	Central Accounting Unit (EC)
CUC	Coal Utilisation Council
CUG	Cadam User Group (computers)

CUG	Calcomp User Group (computers)
CUG	closed user group (computers)
CUG	Computervision User Group (computers)
cupd	cupboard
CURDS	Centre for Urban and Regional Development Studies (Newcastle University)
CUS	Centre for Urban Studies (University College London)
CUUG	Caddie UK User Group
CUV	current-use value
CV	Coventry (postcode area)
CV	curriculum vitae
C-value	thermal conductance
C-VIEW	on-line database: general community information
CVO	confirmation of verbal order
CVWC	Colne Valley Water Company
C/W	clerk of works
CW	cold water
CW	collateral warranty
CW	Crewe (postcode area)
CWC	Cambridge Water Company
CWC	Chester Water Company
CWC	cold water cistern
CWD	Clwyd (BS county code)
CWG	Cooling Water Group (IWS)
CWST	cold water storage tank
CWT	cold water tank
cwt	hundredweight

D

D	500 (Roman numeral)
d	day
d	deci (submultiple prefix: 10^{-1})
d	*denarius* (Lat: penny)
D	depth
D	door
D	dwelling
D	Groundwork (Common Arrangement)
D^2B	domestic digital bus
Da	Danish

DA	Dartford (postcode area)
da	deca (multiple prefix: 10)
DA	development area (DTI assistance)
DA	Diploma in Architecture
DAA	Draughtproofing Advisory Association
DABS	Department of Architecture and Building Science (University of Strathclyde)
DAC	Development Assistance Committee (OECD)

DAF-EM	District Architects Forum – East Midlands		DCW	Design Centre Wales
DAFS	Department of Agriculture and Fisheries for Scotland		DD	designated district (DOE)
DAFS	District Architects Forum for Surrey		DD	draft for development (BSI)
			DD	Dundee (postcode area)
DAMHB	Directorate of Ancient Monuments and Historic Buildings (DOE)		DDIR	Demolition and Dismantling Industry Register
			DDL	data description language (part of DBMS)
DAP	same as PDAP		DDP	district development plan
DAS	defects action sheet (BRE)		DDR	Deutsche Democratische Republik (German Democratic Republic – East Germany)
DAS	Development Advisory Service (World Bank)			
DASD	direct access storage device (computers)		DE	Derby (postcode area)
DASS	digital access signalling system		DEAG	Daylight Extra Action Group
DAT	digital audio tape		Dec	December
DATA	Draughtsmen's and Allied Technicians' Association		Dec	Decorated style
			dec	decimetre
Datel	data telecommunications (British Telecom data transmission facility)		DECT	digital European cordless telephone
			DECUS	Digital Equipment Computer Users Society
			deg	degree (angle)
dB	decibel		deg C	degree Celsius or centigrade
dBA, dB(A)	A-weighted decibel reading		deg F	degree Fahrenheit
DBE	Dame Commander of the British Empire		DE G M & G	*DE Gex MacNaghten & Gordon* (law reports)
DBMS	database management system		del	*delineavit* (Lat: he/she drew it)
DBO	District Building Officer (NHS)		dele	delete
DBR	double bedroom		DELTA	Developing European Learning through Technological Advance
DBY	Derbyshire (BS county code)		delvd	delivered
			DEM	Dialcom Electronic Mail
DC	Design Council		DEn	Department of Energy
DC	developing countries		DEP	Department of Employment and Productivity
DC	Development Commission (now RDC)			
DC	development control		dep	departure
DC	development corporation		dep	deposit
DC	dimensional co-ordination		DEPD	Department of Education and Professional Development (RIBA)
DC, dc	direct current			
DC	Disciplinary Committee (RIBA)		dept	department
DC	district council		DES	Department of Education and Science
DCCC	Domestic Coal Consumers Council			
DCE	data circuit terminating equipment (computers)		DES	Director of Electricity Supply (OER)
			DES(ABB)	Architects and Building Branch, DES
DCE	Direct Contact Exhibitions			
DCF	discounted cash flow		DESI	Division of Economic and Social Information (UN)
DCM	Design Council, Midlands			
DCM	Distinguished Conduct Medal		DesRCA	Designer, Royal College of Art
DCNI	Design Council, Northern Ireland		DETAB	a programming language (computers)
DCNWO	Design Council, North-West Office		DEV	Devon (BS county code)
			DEVCO	ISO Development Committee
DCP	Development Control Panel (RTPI)			
DCTA	see DiCTA		DF	daylight factor

DF	decontamination factor (radiation)
DF	depreciation factor
DF	Development Forum (UN)
DF	drinking fountain
DFC	Distinguished Flying Cross
DFD	Dyfed (BS county code)
DG	Directorate-General (EC)
DG	director-general
DG	Dumfries (postcode area)
DGH	district general hospital
DGHB	Dumfries and Galloway Health Board
DGN	Dungannon, Northern Ireland (BS code)
DGY	Dumfries and Galloway Region, Scotland (BS code)
DH	Durham (postcode area)
D/H	dwellings per hectare
DHA	district health authority (but word 'district' usually omitted from name of individual authority)
DHA	District Heating Association
DHSS	Department of Health and Social Security (now DoH and DSS)
dia	diameter
DIA	Dundee Institute of Architects (RIAS chapter)
diag	diagonal
diam	diameter
DIANE	Direct Information Access Network (EC)
DiCTA	District Councils Technical Association
DIF	data interchange format (computers)
DIN	Deutsche Industrie Normal (German Industry Standard)
DIN	DIN Deutsche Institut für Normung (German Institute for Standardisation)
Dip	diploma
DIP	dual inline package
DIPA	Ductile Iron Pipe Association
DipArch	Diploma in Architecture
DIPC	Ductile Iron Pipe Committee
DipCD	Diploma in Civic Design
DipCons	Diploma in Conservation
DiplArch	Diploma in Architecture
DiplTP	Diploma in Town Planning
DipTP	Diploma in Town Planning
dist	distance

dist	distemper
DistTP	Distinction in Town Planning (RIBA)
div	division, divided
DIY	do it yourself
DJ	*Designers' Journal*
DK	dining kitchen
DL	Darlington, Co Durham (postcode area)
dl	decilitre
DL	envelope size: 110 × 220 mm; for A4 sheet folded into thirds
DLA	Decorative Lighting Association
DLCA	derelict land clearance area (DOE/DTI)
DLF	Disabled Living Foundation
DLO	direct labour organisation
DLPA	Dry Lining and Partition Association
DLR	Docklands Light Railway
DLT	development land tax
DM	Deutsche Mark
DM	dot matrix (printing)
DMA	direct memory access (computers)
DMB	*Development and Materials Bulletin* (GLC; discontinued)
DML	data manipulation language (part of DBMS)
DMS	data management system
DMV	deserted medieval village
DN	design note (DES)
DN	Doncaster, South Yorkshire (postcode area)
dn	down
DNA	deoxyribonucleic acid
DNA	disposal notification area (Community Land Act)
DO	demolition order
do	ditto
DO	drawing office
DOAM	distributed office applications model (computers)
DOBETA	Domestic Oil Burning Equipment Testing Association
doc	document
DOE	Department of the Environment
DoEmp	Department of Employment
DoENI	Department of the Environment for Northern Ireland
DoH	Department of Health

DoI	Department of Industry
DOM/1a	Domestic Subcontract Articles for use with JCT 80 (BEC)
DOM/1c	Domestic Subcontract Conditions for use with JCT 80 (BEC)
DOM/2a	Domestic Subcontract Articles for use with CD 81 (originally DOM/2) (BEC)
DOM/2c	Domestic Subcontract Conditions for use with CD 81 (BEC)
DOM/FR	Formula Rules for Domestic Subcontracts (BEC)
DOMMDA	Drawing Office Material Manufacturers and Dealers Association
DONM	date of next meeting
DOR	Dorset (BS county code)
DOS	disk operating system, disk-based operating system
DOT	Department of Transport
DOW	Down, Northern Ireland (BS code)
doz	dozen
DP	data processing
dp	deep
DP	discharge pipe
DPA	Data Protection Act
DPA	direct professional access (to barristers)
DPAA	Draught Proofing Advisory Association
dpc	dampproof course
DPC	data protection co-ordinator
DPCP	Department of Prices and Consumer Protection
dpi	dots per inch
dpm	dampproof membrane
DPNSS	digital private network signalling system
DPOS	District Planning Officers Society
DPR	Data Protection Registrar
DPWA	Decorative Paving and Walling Association
DR	dining room
dr	door
dr	drain
DRAM	dynamic random access memory (computers)
DRAW	direct read after write (computers)
DRC	depreciated replacement cost
drg	drawing
DRI	Digital Research (California) Incorporated
DRI	driving rain index

DRIVE	Dedicated Road Safety Systems and Intelligent Vehicles in Europe (EC)
DS	Dansk Standardiseringsraad (Danish Standards Organisation)
DS	district surveyor (GLC; superseded by borough building control officer)
DSA	District Surveyors Association (now LDSA)
DSC	Distinguished Service Cross
DSFAAS	Domestic Solid Fuel Appliances Approval Scheme
DSIR	Department of Scientific and Industrial Research
DSM	Distinguished Service Medal
DSMA	Door and Shutter Manufacturers Association
DSO	Distinguished Service Order
DSS	Department of Social Security
DST	daylight saving time
DSWA	Dry Stone Walling Association
DT	Dorchester (postcode area)
DT	draining tap
DTA	differential thermal analysis
DTCD	Department of Technical Co-operation for Development (UNO)
DTE	data terminal equipment
DTI	Department of Trade and Industry
DTL	diode transistor logic (computers)
DTNM	date and time of next meeting
DTp	Department of Transport
DTP	desktop publishing
DTR	double taxation relief
Du	Dutch
DUA	Department of Urban Archaeology
DUG	dBase Users Group (computers)
dup	duplicate
DUR	Durham (BS county code)
DVI	digital video interactive
DVLC	Driver and Vehicle Licensing Centre
dwg	drawing
DWO	district works officer (NHS)
dwt	dead weight tons
DXF	data (or drawing) exchange format (computers)

DY	Dudley, West Midlands (postcode area)	dyn	dyne (CGS unit of force)
Dy	dysprosium (chemical element)	dz	dozen

E

E	east	EARHA	East Anglian Regional Health Authority
E	emissivity (of heat from surface)		
E	energy	EAROM	electrically alterable ROM (computers)
E	envelope (a system of expressing surface flatness)		
		EASA	Ecclesiastical Architects and Surveyors Association
E	erlung (unit of telephone traffic: number of calls per hour × average length)		
		EASN	European Architectural Students Network
E	estimated	EAT	equal appeals tribunal (EOC)
E	exa (multiple prefix: 10^{18})	EAW	Electrical Association for Women
E	In situ concrete/Large precast concrete (Common Arangement)	EAWC	East Anglian Water Company
E	London Eastern (postcode area)	EBCDIC	extended binary coded decimal interchange code
e	the charge on an electron		
E	Young's modulus of elasticity	EBQ	education beyond qualification
ea	each	EC	earth closet
EA	Estates Action programme (DOE)	EC	Electricity Council (1958-89; partly superseded by EAL)
EA	environmental audit		
EAA	Edinburgh Architectural Association (RIAS chapter)	EC	Engineering Council
		EC	Eurocode (EC)
EAA	Electrical Appliance Association	EC	Eurogypsum Congress
EABCC	East Anglian Building Control Consortium	EC	*Euronews Construction* (DOE)
		EC	European Commission
EAC	Engineering Advisory Council	EC	European Community
EAC	European Accident Code (JRC - reactor safety)	EC	European Council
		EC	London Eastern Central (postcode area)
EAC	European Association for Co-operation (EC)		
		ECA	Electrical Contractors Association
EAEC	European Atomic Energy Community (EURATOM)	ECA	Economic Commission for Africa (UN)
EAGGF	European Agricultural Guidance and Guarantee Fund (= FEOGA)	ECA	see CEMBUREAU
		ECA of Scotland	
EAL	Electricity Association Limited		Electrical Contractors Association of Scotland
EAN	European article numbering/number (bar code)	ECC	earth continuity conductor (now called CPC)
E and OE	errors and omissions excepted		
E and W	England and Wales	ECC	ECSC Consultative Committee (EC)
EAP	Environmental Action Programme (EC)		
		ECC	electricity consultative council
EAPROM	electrically alterable programmable ROM (computers)	ECC	Electricity Consumers Council
		ECC	English China Clays

ECC	European Campaign for the Countryside (Council of Europe)
ECC	European Community Committee (RIBA) (formerly 1992 Committee)
ECCE	Environmental Concern Centre in Europe
ECCF	European Committee of Consulting Firms
EC Commission	Commission of the European Communities
ECCS	emergency core cooling system
ECD	Electromagnetic Compatibility Directive (EC)
Ecdin	Environmental Chemical Data and Information Network
ECE	Economic Commission for Europe (UN)
ECE	Export Council for Europe
ECF	European Cultural Foundation
ECGD	Export Credits Guarantee Department (DTI)
ECHO	European Commission Host Organisation (computers)
ECHR	European Commission on Human Rights (Council of Europe)
ECHR	European Court of Human Rights (Council of Europe)
ECI	European Construction Institute (Loughborough)
ECISS	European Committee for Iron and Steel Standardisation
ECJ	European Court of Justice (EC)
ECL	Elstree Computing Limited
ECLAC	Economic Commission for Latin America and the Caribbean (UN)
ECLAIR	European Collaborative Linkage of Agriculture and Industry through Research
ECLSMW	European Convention on the Legal Status of Migrant Workers (Council of Europe)
ECM	European Common Market
ECMA	European Computer Manufacturers Association
ECMC	Electric Cable Makers Confederation
ECME	Economic Commission for the Middle East
ECMT	European Conference of Ministers of Transport
ECMWF	European Centre for Medium-Range Weather Forecasts
ECO	ethylene oxide (oxiran) and chloromethyloxiran (epichloro-hydrin copolymer) (rubber)
ECOSOC	Economic and Social Committee (EC)
ECOSOC	Economic and Social Council (UN)
ECOWAS	Economic Community of West African States
ECPS	Environment and Consumer Protection Service (EC)
ECR	*European Court Reports* (law reports)
ECRC	Electricity Council Research Centre
ECS	European Conservation Strategy (Council of Europe)
ECSC	European Coal and Steel Community (now part of EC)
ECSS	European Code of Social Security (Council of Europe)
ECSS	European Convention on Social Security (Council of Europe)
ECTP	European Council of Town Planners
ECU	European Currency Unit (EC)
ECU	Experimental Cartography Unit (NERC: TIS)
ECV	effective capital value
ECWS	European Centre for Work and Society
ED	ease of decontamination (radiation)
Ed	editor, edited by
Ed, Edn, Edtn	edition
EDA	Electrical Development Association
EDAS	Energy Design Advisory Service
EDC	economic development council
EDC	electricity distribution company
EDCS	Economic Development Co-operative Society (World Bank for Poor Countries)
EDF	European Development Fund (aid for ACP states)
EDI	electronic data interchange
EDICON	Electronic Data Interchange in the Construction Industry
EDIFACT	Electronic Data Interchange for Administration, Commerce and Transport
EDM	electronic distance measuring
EDP	electronic data processing
EDS	Electronic Data Systems (American company)
EDS	exchangeable disk storage
EDSAC	Electronic Delay Storage Automatic Computer (1949)

47

EDTV	extended definition television
EDVAC	Electronic Discrete Variable Automatic Computer (1949)
EE	Early English style
EE	Eastern Electricity
EE	electrical engineer
EE	Enterprise Edinburgh
EEA	Electronic Engineering Association
EEA	European Environmental Agency
EEB	European Environment Bureau
EEC	Environmental Education Committee (RIBA)
EEC	European Economic Community (Common Market – now part of EC)
EED	energy-efficient design
EEF	Engineering Employers Federation
EEFIT	Earthquake Engineering Field Investigation Team
EEIG	European economic interest grouping
EEO	Energy Efficiency Office (DEn)
EEPROM	electronically erasable programmable ROM (computers)
EETPU	Electrical, Electronic, Telecommunications and Plumbing Union (aka EEPTU)
EEY	Energy Efficiency Year (1986)
EFA	effective floor area
EFEP	European Federation of Environmental Professionals
EFILWC	European Foundation for the Improvement of Living and Working Conditions (EC)
EFT	electronic fund transfer
EFTA	European Free Trade Agreement/ Association
EG	*Estates Gazette* (periodical and law reports)
eg	*exempli gratia* (Lat: for example)
EGA	enhanced graphics adaptor (improved version of CGA - computers)
EGCI	Export Group for the Construction Industries
EGCS	*Estates Gazette Case Summaries* (law reports)
EGD	*Estates Gazette Digest of Cases* (law reports)
EGI	effective gross income
EGL	existing ground level
EGLR	*Estates Gazette Law Reports*

EGM	extraordinary general meeting
EH	Edinburgh (postcode area)
EHC	Essex Housing Consortium
EHD	extra high density
EHF	extremely high frequency
EHO	environmental health officer
EHOA	Environmental Health Officers Association
EHSSB	Eastern Health and Social Services Board (Northern Ireland)
EHT	extra high tension
EHV	extra high voltage
EIA	Electronic Industries Association (USA)
EIA	Engineering Industries Association
EIA	environmental impact analysis/ assessment
EIB	European Investment Bank
EIC	Energy Information Centre
EIC	European information centre (EC)
EIDS	European Innovation Diagnosis Scheme (EC)
EIEMA	Electrical Installation Equipment Manufacturers Association
EIS	environmental impact statement
EISA	extended industry standard architecture (computers)
EITB	Engineering Industry Training Board
EJMA	English Joinery Manufacturers Association
EKDC	East Kilbride Development Corporation
EL	electro-level (high-precision measuring device)
el	elevation
el	extra large
EL	eye level
ELB	environment liaison board
ELCB	earth leakage circuit breaker
elec	electricity, electrical
ELEC	European League for Economic Co-operation
elev	elevation
ELF	extremely low frequency
Eliz	Elizabeth, Elizabethan
ELOT	Hellenic Organisation for Standardisation
elp	extra large pipe

ELR	equal listener response scale (acoustics)
ELRC	East London River Crossing
ELSI	extra large scale integration (computers)
em	electromagnetic
EMA	Engineers and Managers Association
EMA	European Monetary Agreement
Email	electronic mail
EMCF	European Monetary Co-operation Fund (EC)
EME	East Midlands Electricity
emf	electromotive force
EMF	European Monetary Fund
EMI	electromagnetic interference
EML	expanded metal lathing
EMP	electromagnetic pulse
EMR	electromagnetic resonance
EMRBCC	East Midlands Region Building Control Consortium
EMS	energy management system (computers)
EMS	European Monetary System (EC)
EMU	Economic and Monetary Union (EC)
emu	electromagnetic unit
emuls	emulsion (paint)
EN	Enfield (postcode area)
EN	enforcement notice
EN	Euronorm (European standard) (EC)
ENBRI	European Network of Building Research Institutes (EC)
enc, encl	enclosed, enclosure
ENDOC	on-line database: listing of environmental information and documentation centres in member states of EC
ENE	east-north-east
ENEA	European Nuclear Energy Agency
Eng	engineer
eng	engineering
Eng	England, English
ENIAC	Electronic Numerical Integrator and Calculator (1946 – first electronic computer)
ENIU	Ente Nazionale Italiano di Unificazione (Italian National Standards Organisation)
ENREP	on-line database: information on environmental research projects in EC
E number	EC coding for food additives
ENV	European prestandard (EC)
EO	extra over
EOC	Equal Opportunities Commission
EOEC	European Organisation for Economic Co-operation (= OECE)
EONR	European Organisation for Nuclear Research
EOQC	European Organisation for Quality Control
EOTP	European Organisation for Trade Promotion
EP	elderly person
EP	electro-plated
EP	epoxy, epoxide resin
E/P	ethylene propylene
EP	European Parliament
EPA	Environmental Protection Agency (USA)
EPA	Equal Pay Act
EPA	European Productivity Agency (OEEC)
EPC	Energy Policy Committee (RIBA)
EPC	European Patent Convention
EPC	European Political Co-operation
EPC	European Population Committee (Council of Europe)
EPCIA	Expanded Polystyrene Cavity Insulation Association
EPD	education and professional development (see also DEPD)
EPDC	Education and Professional Development Committee (RIBA)
EPDM	ethylene propylene diene terpolymer (rubber)
EPEA	Electrical Power Engineers Association
EPG	Energy Policy Group (RIBA)
EPH	elderly persons' home
EPI	employers' protection insurance
EPM	ethylene-propylene copolymer (rubber)
EPNdB	effective perceived noise decibel
EPOC	Equal Pay and Opportunities Campaign
EPOC	Equal Pay and Opportunities Commission
EPRI	Edison Power Research Institute (USA)
EPROM	erasable programmable ROM (computers)
EPS	expanded polystyrene
EPT	excess profits tax
EPTA	Expanded Programme of Technical Assistance (UNO)
EPU	European Payments Union

49

Eq	*Equity* (law reports)
EQUAL	Engineering Contractors Quality Assurance
equiv	equivalent
ER	*Elizabeth Regina*
ER	*English Reports* (law reports)
Er	erbium (chemical element)
ERA	Electrical Research Association
ERA	ERA Technology
ERASMUS	European Community Action Scheme for the Mobility of University Students (EC)
ERBE	Earth Radiation Budget Experiment
ERC	Electronics Research Council
ERDF	European Regional Development Fund (EC)
ERDS	European Reliability Data System (JRC – reactor safety)
EREG	Eastern Region Energy Group for the Building Professions
ERG	Ecology Research Group
erg	unit of energy
ERM	exchange rate mechanism (EMS)
ERMES	Euromessage (international message paging consortium)
ERNIE	Electronic Random Number Indicator Equipment
ERO	emergency relief organisation
EROM	erasable ROM (computers)
ERS	Electoral Reform Society
ERS	Engineering Research Station (British Gas)
ERU	Energy Research Unit (Leeds Polytechnic)
ERV	estimated rental value
Es	einsteinium (chemical element)
ES	environmental statement
ESA	environmentally-sensitive area
ESA	European Space Agency
ESA	European Supply Agency
ESA/1	Employer/Specialist Agreement (JCT form)
ESA-IRS	European Space Agency Information Retrieval System
ESC	Economic and Social Committee (ECOSOC) (EC)
ESC	Economic and Social Council (ECOSOC) (UN)
ESC	Engineering Standards Committee (1901; forerunner of BSI)

ESC	European Social Charter (Council of Europe)
ESCAP	Economic and Social Commission for Asia and the Pacific (UN)
ESCWA	Economic and Social Commission for Western Asia (UN)
ESD	Excluded Sectors Directive (EC) (see Wet)
ESDEP	European Steel Design Education Programme
ESDP	European Social Development Programme (UN)
ESDU	Engineering Sciences Data Unit (now ESDU International)
ESE	east-south-east
ESF	European Social Fund (EC)
ESOP	employees share ownership plan
ESP	environmental system performance (computer program)
esp	especially
ESPRIT	European Strategic Research Programme in Information Technology (EC)
Esq	Esquire
ESR	essential safety requirements (EC)
ESRO	European Space Research Organisation
ESS	Essex (BS county code)
ESSP	employers' statutory sick pay
EST	earliest start time
EST	Eastern Standard Time
Est	established
est	estimated
ESTA	Energy Systems Trade Association
ESTI	European Solar Test Installation
esu	electrostatic unit
ESWC	East Surrey Water Company
ESX	East Sussex (BS county code)
ET	emerging technology
ET	Employment Training (government scheme)
ETA	estimated time of arrival
ETA	European technical approval (EC)
et al	*et alibi* (Lat: and elsewhere)
et al	*et alii, alia* (Lat: and other people, things)
et al	*et aliter* (Lat: and otherwise)
ETB	English Tourist Board
ETC	Ecological Trading Company
ETC	environmental test centre
etc	*et cetera* (Lat: and the rest, and so on)
ETD	Energy Technology Division (DEn)
ETD	expected time of departure

ETI	economic thickness of insulation
ETS	European technical specification (EC)
et seq	*et sequens* (Lat: and what follows)
ETSI	European Telecommunications Standards Institute (CEPT)
ETSU	Energy Technology Support Unit (DEn – Harwell Laboratory)
ETU	Electrical Trades Union
ETUC	European Trade Union Confederation
ETUI	European Trade Union Institute
Eu	euler number (fluid dynamics)
Eu	europium (chemical element)
EU	polyether rubber
EUA	European Unit of Account (replaced by ECU in 1981) (EC)
EUC	established use certificate
EURA	Energy Users Research Association
EURAM	European Research on Advanced Materials (EC)
EURATOM	European Atomic Energy Community (now part of EC)
EUREKA	European Research Co-ordination Agency
EUREMA	European counterpart of Eurisol
Euring	environmental database (EC)
Eurisol	Eurisol UK (UK Mineral Wool Association)
EURO-CO-OP	European Community of Consumer Co-operatives
EUROFER	European Confederation of the Iron and Steel Industry
EUROFEU	European equivalent of FIC
EUROKOM	Teleconferencing and Electronic Mail System (ESPRIT)
Euronet-Diane	
	Direct Information Access Network for Europe (EC)
EUROSAG	European Salaried Architects Group
EUROSMI	European Committee for Small and Medium-sized Industry
EUROSTAT	Statistical Office of the European Communities

EURIDICE	Education Information Network in the European Community
EUV	existing use value
ev	electron volt
EVA	as EVAC
EVAC	emergency visual audio control
EVAC	ethylene vinyl acetate copolymer
EVCA	European Venture Capital Association
evg	evening
EVIT	emergency video intelligent terminal
EVP	electronic voice phenomena
EVT	equi-viscous temperature
e'ware	earthenware
EWC	Eastbourne Water Company
EWC	Essex Water Company
EWC	European Water Charter (Council of Europe)
EWC	expected week of confinement (SMP)
EWIA	External Wall Insulation Association
EWO	essential works order
EWR	Electricity at Work Regulations
EWWC	East Worcestershire Water Company
ex	exceeding
Ex	Exchequer
EX	Exeter (postcode area)
ex	out of
exc	excavate
exc, excl	exclude, excluding
Exch	*Exchequer Reports* (law reports)
EXCO	ISO Executive Committee
ex div	ex dividend (without dividend)
ex off	*ex officio* (Lat: by virtue of one's office)
exp	exposed
ext	extension (telephone number)
ext	exterior, external
extg	existing
EZ	enterprise zone

F	Fahrenheit
F	farad (unit of capacitance)
F	fellow
F	female
f	femto (submultiple prefix: 10^{-15})
F	firm or fine (pencil lead grade; replaced by HB)
F	flat (dwelling)
F	fluorine (chemical element)
f	following (page)
F	force
f	frequency
F	Friday
F	Masonry (Common Arrangement)
Fac	faculty
FACE	International Federation of Computer Users in Engineering, Architecture and related fields
FACT	Federation Against Copyright Theft
FAI	fresh air inlet
F&ExpT	header feed and expansion tank
F&GPC	finance and general purposes committee
FAO	Food and Agriculture Organisation (UN)
fao	for the attention of
FAO	fresh air outlet
FAP	first aid post
FAS	Faculty of Architects and Surveyors (now ASI)
FASI	Fellow of the Architects and Surveyors Institute
FASS	Federation of Associations of Specialists and Subcontractors
fast	fastener
FAST	Federation Against Software Theft
FAST	Forecasting and Assessment in Science and Technology (EC)
FAT	file allocation table (computers)
fax	facsimile
FB	Faculty of Building
FB	flush bracket (OS bench mark)
FBA	Farm Buildings Association (FBIC)
FBAC	Farm Buildings Advisory Committee (Design Centre)
FBBDO	see Fidor
FBBI	Fibre Building Board Industry

FBC	Federation of Brickwork Contractors
FBCEC	Federation of Building and Civil Engineering Contractors (NI) (Northern Ireland)
FBCMA	Fibre Bonded Carpet Manufacturers Association
FBD	Farm Buildings Department (West of Scotland Agricultural College)
FBE	fusion-bonded epoxy (reinforcement coating)
FBEAMA	see BEAMA
FBFO	Federation of British Fire Organisations
FBI	Federation of British Industry (now merged with CBI)
FBIC	Farm Buildings Information Centre (NAC)
FBM	fundamental bench mark (OS)
FBSC	Federation of Building Specialist Contractors
FBU	Fire Brigades Union
FC	flushing cistern
FC	Forestry Commission
FCA	Fencing Contractors Association
FCA	fuel cost adjustment
FCEC	Federation of Civil Engineering Contractors
fcgs	facings
FCIArb	Fellow of the Chartered Institute of Arbitrators
FCIOB	Fellow of the Chartered Institute of Building
FCMA	Fibre Cement Manufacturers Association
FCO	Foreign and Commonwealth Office
FCSD	Fellow of the Chartered Society of Designers
FDC	Federation of Dredging Contractors
FDM	frequency-division multiplexing (telecommunications)
fdn	foundation
FDRI	fire damage rating index (forestry)
FDWC	Folkstone and District Water Company
Fe	ferrum (iron – chemical element)

FEANI	European Federation of National Engineering Associations
Feb	February
Fed	federation
FEDCAD	Federation of CAD User Groups
fem	female, feminine
FEng	Fellowship of Engineering
FEOGA	Fond Européen d'Orientation et de Garanti Agricole (= EAGGF)
FEP	fluorinated ethylene propylene, perfluoroethylene propylene
FEPD	Fire and Emergency Planning Department (Home Office)
FER	Fermanagh, Northern Ireland (BS code)
FeRFA	Federation of Resin Formulators and Applicators
FES	family expenditure survey
FET	field effect transistor (computers)
FETA	Fire Extinguishing Trades Association
ff	fair faced
ff	following (pages)
FFAS	Fellow of the Faculty of Architects and Surveyors – architect (now FASI)
FFB	Fellow of the Faculty of Building
FFC	Friends of Friendless Churches
FFL	finished floor level
FFPS	Fauna and Flora Preservation Society
FFR	flux fraction ratio (lighting)
FFS	Fellow of the Faculty of Architects and Surveyors – surveyor (now FASI)
FGMA	Flat Glass Manufacturers Association
FGPC	finance and general purposes committee
FGR	Federal German Republic (West Germany)
FH	fire hydrant
FHANG	Federation of Heathrow Anti-Noise Groups
FHB	Fife Health Board
FIA	Fencing Industry Association
FIAA	Fellow Architect of the Incorporated Association of Architects and Surveyors
FIAA&S	Fellow Architect and Surveyor of the Incorporated Association of Architects and Surveyors
FIAS	Fellow Surveyor of the Incorporated Association of Architects and Surveyors
FIBS	financial incentive bonus scheme (work study)
FIC	Fire Industry Council
FID	Fédération Internationale d'Information et de Documentation
FIDIC	Fédération Internationale des Ingénieurs Conseils (International Federation of Consulting Engineers)
Fidor	Fibre Building Board Development Organisation
FIEC	European Construction Industry Federation
FIF	Fife Region, Scotland (BS code)
FIFO	first in first out (electronic mail)
fig	figure
fin	finish, finished
FINDEX	facet-orientated indexing system for architecture and construction engineering
FIOA	Fellow of the Institute of Acoustics
FIP	Fédération Internationale de la Précontrainte
FIPACE	International Federation of Self-generating Industrial Users of Electricity
FIPMEC	International Federation of Small and Medium-sized Enterprises
FIRA	Furniture Industry Research Association
FIRTO	Fire Insurers Research and Testing Organisation
FISA	Finance Industry Standards Association
FK	Falkirk (postcode area)
fl	flourished
FL	frost resistant and with low soluble salt content (bricks)
FLAIR	Food-linked Agro-Industrial Research (EC)
fl&b	framed, ledged and braced
FLAS	Fellow of the Land Agents Society
Flem	Flemish bond
FLI	Fellow of the Landscape Institute
fl oz	fluid ounce
FLR	flame retardant
flr	floor
Fm	fermium (chemical element)
FM	frequency modulation
FMB	Federation of Master Builders

FMCEC	Federation of Manufacturers of Construction Equipmemt and Cranes
FMPA	formula method of price adjustment
fmwk	formwork
FN	frost resistant and with normal soluble salt content (bricks)
fndn	foundation
FNF	fault not found
FNSCC	Federation of Nuclear Shelter Consultants and Contractors
f number	relative aperture of camera etc
F/O	fix only
fob	free on board
FOC	Fire Offices Committee
FOC	free of charge
FoE	Friends of the Earth
FoEng	Fellowship of Engineering
FOG	frequency of gobbledegook
FOR	Fire Officers' Recommendations
FORTH	a high level programming language designed for small computers
FORTRAN	formula translation (a computer programming language)
FOTS	fibre optics transmission system
fp	freezing point
FPA	Fire Precautions Act
FPA	Fire Protection Association
FPDA	Finnish Plywood Development Association
FPI	Finnish Plywood International
FPM	rubber having fluoro and fluoroalkyl substituent groups on the polymer chain
FPO	fire prevention officer
FPS	Fauna Preservation Society
FPS	Federation of Piling Specialists
FR	flame resistant
FR	formula rules (JCT)
fr	frame
fr	franc
Fr	French
Fr	francium (chemical element)
FRA	Flexible Roofing Association
FRCAB	Flat Roofing Contractors Advisory Board
FRED	fast reactor experiment Dounreay
FRG	Federal Republic of Germany (West Germany)
Fri	Friday
FRI	full repairing and insuring (lease)
FRI	Fulmer Research Institute

FRIAS	Fellow of the Royal Incorporation of Architects in Scotland
FRIBA	Fellow of the Royal Institute of British Architects
FRICS	Fellow of the Royal Institution of Chartered Surveyors
FRIDA	Fund for Research and Investment for the Development of Africa
Frontiers	forecasting rain optimised using new techniques of interactively enhanced radar and satellite data (MO)
FRP	as FRTP
FRPB	Forth River Purification Board
FRS	Fellow of the Royal Society
FRS	Fire Research Station (part of BRE)
FRSA	Fellow of the Royal Society of Arts
FRSE	Fellow of the Royal Society Edinburgh
FRTP	(fibre) reinforced thermoplastic
FRTPI	Fellow of the Royal Town Planning Institute
FRV	full rental value
FS	floorspace
FS	fluctuations supplement (JCT)
FS	foul sewer
FS	Fountains Society
FSA	Fellow of the Society of Antiquaries
FSA	Fylde Society of Architects (RIBA Blackpool branch)
FSAI	Fellow of the Society of Architectural Illustrators
FSAVC	free-standing additional voluntary contributions scheme (pensions)
FSC	Field Studies Council
FSC	Fire Service College
FS/D	floorspace per dwelling
FS/H	floorspace per hectare
FSI	Fire Service Inspectorate
fsnr	fastener
FSR	*Fleet Street Reports* (law reports)
ft	foot, feet
FTA	Freight Transport Association
FTAM	file transfer access and management (computers)
FTAT	Furniture, Timber and Allied Trades Union
FTB	first time (house) buyer
FTSE	*Financial Times* Stock Exchange financial index

FUME	Foam Upholstery Must End	fwd	forward
FUMPO	Federated Union of Managerial and Professional Officers	FWH	flexible working hours
		FWRMGB	Federation of Wire Rope Manufacturers of Great Britain
fur	furlong		
furn	furniture		
		fxd	fixed
FVHB	Forth Valley Health Board	fxg	fixing
FWA	Factories and Workshops Act	FY	Blackpool (postcode area)

G

g	acceleration due to free fall; standard gravity	GC	general contractor
		GC	George Cross
G	gas plug-in point	GC	government contract
G	giga (multiple prefix: 10^9)	GCB	Knight of the Bath (GC = Grand Cross)
g	girth		
G	Glasgow (postcode area)	GCC	Gas Consumers Council
g	gram (unit of mass)	GCC	Gulf Co-operation Council
G	ground floor	GCCNI	General Consumer Council for Northern Ireland (electricity)
G	gully		
G	maximum gap	GCE	General Certificate of Education
g	minimum gap	gcf	greatest common factor
G	Structural/Carcassing metal/ timber (Common Arrangement)	GCS	Geospace Consultancy Systems
		GCSE	General Certificate of Secondary Education
G7	Group of Seven leading industrialised countries	GC/Works/1	General Conditions of Contract for Building and Civil Engineering
Ga	gallium (chemical element)	GC/Works/2	minor works version of GC/ Works/1
GA	Galvanisers Association		
GA	General Assembly (UN)	Gd	gadolinium (chemical element)
GA	Geographical Association	GD	General Directive (EC)
GA	Geologists Association	GDC	Glenrothes Development Corporation
GAA	Gloucestershire Architectural Association (RIBA branch)		
		Gdns	Gardens
GAD	Gas Appliances Directive (EC)	GDO	General Development Order
GAI	Guild of Architectural Ironmongers	GDP	gross domestic product
		GDR	German Democratic Republic (East Germany)
gal	gallon		
galv	galvanised	GDS	graphics design system (CAD system)
GAS	GRP Advisory Service		
GATT	General Agreement on Tariffs and Trade (UN)	Ge	germanium (chemical element)
		GEI	General and Engineering Industries
GAYE	Give As You Earn		
		GEM	graphic environment manager (DRI system – computers)
GB	Great Britain		
gbdp	galvanised barrel distance piece	GEMS	Global Environmental Monitoring System (UN)
GBE	Knight or Dame of the British Empire (G = Grand Cross)		

55

gen	general
genset	generator set
geog	geography
geol	geology
geom	geometry
Ger	Germany, German
GeV	giga electron volts
GF	ground floor
GFTHTA	Glazed and Floor Tile Home Trade Association
GFTU	General Federation of Trade Unions
GG	Georgian Group
GGBS	ground granulated blastfurnace slag
GGF	Glass and Glazing Federation
GGHB	Greater Glasgow Health Board
GHB	Grampian Health Board
GHS	general household survey
GI	galvanised iron
GIA	general improvement area
GIA	Glasgow Institute of Architects (RIAS chapter)
GIFA	gross internal floor area
Giff	*Gifford* (law reports)
GIG	General Information Group (DOE)
GIGO	garbage in garbage out (computers)
GIS	geographic information system
Gk	Greek
GKN	Guest, Keen and Nettlefolds
GKS	graphical kernal system (computers)
GL	Gloucester (postcode area)
GL	ground level
GLAC	Greater London Architecture Club
GLAD	Greater London Association for the Disabled
GLC	Greater London Council (1965-86)
GLDP	Greater London Development Plan
GLS	general lighting service (normal pear-shaped electric light bulb)
GLSMR	Greater London Sites and Monuments Record
glzg	glazing
GM	general manager
GM	George Medal

g/m^2	grams per square metre (weight of paper)
GMB	General, Municipal, Boilermakers and Allied Trades Union
GMBATU	see GMB
GmbH	gessellschaft mit beschränkter haftung (Ger: limited liability company)
GMF	Glass Manufacturers Federation
GMP	Grampian Region, Scotland (BS code)
GMT	Greenwich Mean Time
GMWU	General and Municipal Workers Union
GNP	gross national product
GNT	Gwent (BS county code)
G of S	Guild of Surveyors
GOM	grand old man
GOSIP	Government OSI Profile (computers)
goth	Gothic style
govt	government
GP	glazed pipe
GPC	general purposes committee
GPCSA	General Practice Computer Suppliers Association
GPDA	Gypsum Products Development Association
GPO	copolymer of propylene oxide and allyl glycidyl ether (rubber)
GPO	General Post Office (now PO)
GRACE	graphic arts composing equipment (computers)
grad	graduate
grano	granolithic
GRC	glass reinforced cement
GRCA	Glassfibre Reinforced Cement Association
GRID	Global Resource Information Database (UN)
GRIM	glass reflected index measurement
GRIM	Group on Regulations, Information and Management (EC)
grnds	grounds
GRP	glass (fibre) reinforced plastic or polyester based on a thermosetting resin
GRS	Gloucestershire (BS county code)
GRT	gross registered tonnes
grve	groove

GS	general structural (structural softwood classification)		GTS	general thinking skills
gs	general surfaces		GU	Guildford, Surrey (postcode area)
GS	Geographical Survey		guar	guaranteed
GS	Geological Survey		GUG	Gable User Group (computers)
GS	see G of S		GUG	GDS User Group (computers)
GSA	Guernsey Society of Architects		GUG	Gintran User Group (computers)
GSLB	Group Special Large Bands (communications working group)		G value	unit used in radiation chemistry
gsm	grams per square metre (weight of paper)		GWH	gas water heater
GSP	Generalised System of Preferences (tariffs for developing countries)		GWN	Gwynedd (BS county code)
			GWP	glazed-ware pipe
			GW/S	Government Works Subcontract
GSR	GCS stereometric radar		GW/Sa	Government Works Subcontract Articles of Agreement and Appendix (BEC)
GSS	Government Statistical Service			
GSX	graphics system extension (computers)		GW/Sc	Government Works Subcontract Conditions (BEC)
GSY	Guernsey (BS code)		GW/S/FR	Government Works Subcontract Price Adjustment Formula Provisions
GT	grease trap			
Gt Brit	Great Britain			
GTM	Greater Manchester (BS county code)		Gy	gray (unit of radiation dose)

H

H	Cladding/Covering (Common Arrangement)		HACAN	Heathrow Association for the Control of Aircraft Noise
H	enthalpy (thermodynamic)		HAG	housing action grant
H	hard (pencil lead grade)		HAG	housing action group
h	hecto (multiple prefix: 10^2)		HAM	Hampshire (BS county code)
H	height		HAN	housing association note
H	henry (unit of inductance)		h&c	hot and cold (water)
H	hot (water)		H&CWT	combined water storage tank
h	hour		HAPA	Handicapped Adventure Playground Association
H	house			
H	humidifier		HARP	heating and rent payment
H	hydrant		HASS	home accident surveillance system
H	hydrogen (chemical element)			
h	Planck's constant (energy)		HAT	housing action trust
H_2O	water		HB	half brick
H_2SO_4	sulphuric acid		HB	hard-black (average pencil lead grade)
HA	Harrow, Middlesex (postcode area)		HB	hose bib
			HBB	Historic Buildings Board
ha	hectare (100 a, or 10 000 m^2)		HBCS	Historic Buildings Council for Scotland
HAA	Hertfordshire Association of Architects (RIBA branch)		HBC(W)	Historic Buildings Council for Wales
HAC	high alumina (content) cement			

57

HBF	House Builders Federation
HBG	Historic Buildings Group
HBMCE	Historic Buildings and Monuments Commission for England
HBN	hospital building note
hbs	herring-bone strutting
hc	hardcore
HC	Heritage Conserved
hc	hot and cold (water)
HC	House of Commons
HC	Housing Corporation
HCAS	Housing Corporation Association in Scotland (now merged with SSHA as Scottish Homes)
HCF	Henley Centre for Forecasting
hcf	highest common factor
HCH	hexachlorocylohexane
HCHS	hospital and community health services
HCIMA	Hotel Catering and Institutional Management Association
HCl	hydrochloric acid
h'core	hardcore
HCP	Housing Corporation paper
HCPT	Historic Churches Preservation Trust
HCSP	Housing Campaign for Single People
HCT	Housing Centre Trust
HCY	housing cost yardstick
HD	harmonisation document (EC)
HD	high density
HD	Huddersfield (postcode area)
hdb	hardboard
hd'bd	hardboard
HDD	Housing Development Directorate
HDD:OP	HDD occasional paper
hdg	heading
HDN	housing development note
HDPE	high density polyethylene
HDTV	high definition television
He	helium (chemical element)
HE	high explosive
HEA	Health Education Authority (formerly HEC)
HEBA	Home Extension Building Association
HEC	Health Education Council (now HEA)
HEC	Home Extension Consultancy
HESA	Hot Extruded Sealant Association

Hf	hafnium (chemical element)
HF	high frequency
HFL	Homes Fit to Live in (CBR and HCSP joint scheme)
HG	Harrogate, North Yorkshire (postcode area)
Hg	hydrargyrum (mercury - chemical element)
HGV	heavy goods vehicle
HH	double-hard (pencil lead grade)
HHB	Highland Health Board
hi	high
HID	Heritage in Danger
HIDB	Highlands and Islands Development Board
hi-fi	high fidelity
HIG	Hazardous Installations Group (HSE)
HIP	housing investment programme
HIS	Homes Insulation Scheme
HK	Hong Kong
HL	House of Lords
HLD	Highland Region, Scotland (BS code)
HLR	*House of Lords Reports* (law reports)
HM	His/Her Majesty/Majesty's
HME	high density medium board - extra density
HMFI	HM Factory Inspectorate
HMG	HM Government
HMI	HM Immigration
HMI	HM Inspector
HMIAPI	HM Industrial Air Pollution Inspectorate
HMIP	HM Inspectorate of Pollution
HMLR	HM Land Registry
HMN	high density medium board - normal density
HMO	house in multiple occupation
hmsf	hand made sand faced
HMSO	HM Stationery Office
HMWPE	high molecular weight polyethylene
hn&w	head nut and washer
HNC	Higher National Certificate
HND	Higher National Diploma
Ho	holmium (chemical element)
HO	Home Office
ho	house

HOCPC	Home Office Crime Prevention Centre
HOCUS	hand or computer universal simulator (computer system)
HOFD	Home Office Fire Department
Hon	honorary
Hon	Honourable
Hons	Honours
Hon Sec	honorary secretary
Hon Treas	honorary treasurer
horiz	horizontal
Hort	horticulture, horticultural
hosp	hospital
HOWL	Hands Off Wildlife
HP	Hemel Hempstead, Hertfordshire (postcode area)
hp	high pressure
HP	hire purchase
hp	horsepower
HP	Houses of Parliament
HPACB	Heat Pump and Air-Conditioning Bureau
HPDA	Housing Project Design Awards
HPMA	Heat Pump Manufacturers Association
HPW	house party wall
HQ	headquarters
HR	habitable room
HR	half round
HR	Hereford (postcode area)
hr	hour
HR	Hydraulics Research
HRA	habitable rooms per acre
HRA	housing renewal area
HRC	high rupturing capacity (electric fuse)
HR/D	habitable rooms per dwelling
HRDG	Human Resource Development Group (Commonwealth)
HRF	hot-rolled flats (steel)
HRF	Housing Research Foundation
HR/H	habitable rooms per hectare
HRH	His/Her Royal Highness
HRPA	Historic Royal Palaces Agency
HRPB	Highland River Purification Board
HRT	Hertfordshire (BS county code)
HSA	Health and Safety Agency for Northern Ireland
HSA	Herefordshire Society of Architects (RIBA branch)
HSA	Huddersfield Society of Architects (RIBA branch)

HSANI	Health and Safety Agency for Northern Ireland
HSAU	Housing Service Advisory Unit (DOE)
HSC	Health and Safety Commission
HSC	Higher School Certificate
HSC	Hospital Safety Commission
HSD	Hazardous Substances Division (HSE)
hsd	housed
HSE	Health and Safety Executive
hse	house
HSELIS	HSE Library and Information Services
hses	houses
HSFG	high strength friction grip (bolts)
HST	high speed train
HSW	health and safety at work
ht	height
HT	high tension
HTFEN	Historic Towns Forum of Europa Nostra
HTFS	Heat Transfer and Fluid Flow Service (Harwell)
HTGR	high temperature gas-cooled reactor
HTL	hearing threshold level
HTLG	Humberside Technical Liaison Group
HTM	health/hospital technical memorandum
HTTA	Highway and Traffic Technicians Association
HU	Hull (postcode area)
HUG	Harris User Group (computers)
HUM	Humberside (BS county code)
HV	high velocity
HV	high voltage
HVCA	Heating and Ventilating Contractors Association
HW	hardwood
HW	high water
hw	hollow wall
HW	hot water
HWC	Hartlepools Water Company
HWC	hot water cylinder
hwd	hardwood
HWLB	high water London Bridge
HWM	high water mark
HWR	heavywater reactor
HWR	Hereford and Worcester (BS county code)

59

HWT	hot water tank	HYDSA	Harrogate and Yorkshire Dales Society of Architects (RIBA branch)
Hwy	highway		
HX	Halifax, West Yorkshire (postcode area)	Hz	hertz (unit of frequency)

I

I	1 (Roman numeral)	IARC	International Agency for Research on Cancer
I	current (rate of flow of electricity)	IAS	immediate access store (computers)
I	iodine (chemical element)		
I	Island, Isle	IASC	International Accounting and Standards Committee
IA	improvement area		
IA	Institute of Actuaries	IAT	Institute of Asphalt Technology
IA	Institute of Agriculture	IAT	international atomic time
IA	intermediate area (DTI assistance)	IATA	International Air Transport Association
IAA	Inverness Architectural Association (RIAS chapter)	IAWA	International Archive of Women in Architecture (Virginia, USA)
IAA	International Academy of Architecture		
IAAS	Incorporated Association of Architects and Surveyors	IB	industrialised building
		IB	Institute of Building (now CIOB)
IAAS	Institute of Advanced Architectural Studies (University of York)	IB	International Bank
		IBA	Independent Broadcasting Authority
IABSE	International Association for Bridge and Structural Engineering, British Group	IBA	industrial building allowance
		IBB	Invest in Britain Bureau (DTI)
IAC	Industrial Acoustics Company	IBC	Institute of Building Control
IACPS	International Advisory Committee on Pollution of the Sea	IBC	Integrated Broadband Communication (EC: RACE)
		IBCC	International Building Classification Committee
IAEA	International Atomic Energy Authority (UN)	IBCO	Institution of Building Control Officers
IAI	Institute of Architectural Ironmongers	IBE	Institution of British Engineers
IAL	international algebraic language (computers)	IBEC	International Bank for Economic Co-operation (same membership as COMECON)
IAM	Institute of Administrative Management	IBG	Industrial Biocide Group (BACS)
IAMAP	International Association of Meteorology and Atmospheric Physics	IBG	Institute of British Geographers
		IBG	inter-block gap (computers)
		IBICC	Incorporated British Institute of Certified Carpenters
IAPI	Industrial Air Pollution Inspectorate	ibid	*ibidem* (Lat: in the same place)
IAPMO	International Association of Plumbing and Mechanical Officials	IBM	Institute of Builders Merchants
		IBM	International Business Machines Corporation
IAR	instruction address register (computers)	IBN	Institut Belge de Normalisation (Belgian Institute for Standardisation)
IArb	Institute of Arbitrators		

IBPGR	International Board for Plant Genetic Resources
IBRD	International Bank for Reconstruction and Development (World Bank) (UN)
IBRM	Institute of Baths and Recreation Management
i/c	in charge
IC	inspection chamber
IC	integrated circuit
IC	see ICeram
ICA	Institute of Chartered Accountants
ICA	Institute of Company Accountants
ICA	Institute of Contemporary Arts
ICA	Inter City Aid
ICAM	International Confederation of Architectural Museums
ICAO	International Civil Aviation Organisation (UN)
ICBP	International Council for Bird Protection
ICC	International Chamber of Commerce
ICCG	Interdepartmental Component Co-ordination Group (renamed ICDG)
ICDG	Interdepartmental Construction Development Group (previously ICCG)
ICE	Institution of Civil Engineers
ICE	internal combustion engine
ICeram	Institute of Ceramics
ICFE	International Contract Flooring Exhibition
ICFTU	International Conference of Free Trade Unions
IChemE	Institution of Chemical Engineers
ICI	Imperial Chemical Industries
ICID	International Commission on Irrigation and Drainage (FAO)
ICJ	International Court of Justice (World Court) (UN)
ICJ	*International Court of Justice Law Reports*
ICL	International Computers Limited
ICMA	Institute of Cost and Management Accountants
ICOM	Industrial Common Ownership Movement
ICOMOS	International Council of Monuments and Sites
ICONDA	CIB International Construction Database

ICorrST	Institution of Corrosion Science and Technology
ICPA	inner city partnership area
ICPU	Inner Cities Policy Unit (DOE)
ICPUG	Independent Commodore Products Users Group (computers)
ICR	*Industrial Cases/Court Reports* (law reports)
ICRA	International Cancer Research Agency
ICRF	Imperial Cancer Research Fund
ICRP	International Commission on Radiological Protection
ICS	ISVR Consultancy Services
ICSA	Institute of Chartered Secretaries and Administrators
ICST	Imperial College of Science and Technology
ICSTD	Intergovernmental Committee on Science and Technology for Development (UN)
ICSTIS	Independent Committee for the Supervision of Television Information Services
ICT	Institute of Concrete Technology
ICT	International Computers and Tabulators
ICW	Institute of Clerks of Works of Great Britain Incorporated
id	*idem* (Lat: the same)
ID	identity, proof of identity
I/D	inside diameter
ID	interior design
ID	*Interior Design*
ID	interpretative document (EC)
IDA	integrated digital access (telecommunications)
IDA	International Development Association (UN)
IDB	Industrial Development Board
IDB	Inter-American Development Bank
IDB	Islamic Development Bank
IDC	industrial development certificate (now defunct)
IDC	International Data Corporation (computers)
IDC	Irving Development Corporation
IDCPF	Inter-Departmental Committee on Professional Fees
IDD	international direct dialling
IDDA	Interior Decorators and Designers Association
IDEA	Innovation Development European Appraisal (EC)

IDHE	Institute of Domestic Heating and Environmental Engineers
IDN	integrated digital network (telecommunications)
IDP	integrated data processing
IDPM	Institute of Data Processing Management
IDPS	*Interior Design Product Selector*
IDS	Institute of Development Studies
IDT	industrial design technology
IDTV	improved definition television
ie	*id est* (Lat: that is)
IE	Institute of Energy
IEA	International Energy Agency (OECD)
IEC	International Electrotechnical Commission (CEI) (electrotechnical counterpart of ISO)
IED	Institution of Engineering Designers
IED	integrated environmental design
IEDO	Institution of Economic Development Officers
IEE	Institution of Electrical Engineers
IEEE	a standard interface (IEEE – computers)
IEEE	Institute of Electrical and Electronics Engineers (USA)
IEEIE	Institution of Electrical and Electronics Incorporated Engineers
IEETE	Institution of Electrical and Electronics Technician Engineers
IEHO	Institution of Environmental Health Officers
IERE	Institute of Electronic and Radio Engineers
IES	Illuminating Engineering Society
IET	Institute of Engineers and Technicians
IExpE	Institute of Explosives Engineers
IF	intermediate frequency
IFAD	International Fund for Agricultural Development (UN)
IFAN	International Federation for the Application of Standards
IfBt	Institut für Bautechnik (West Germany)
IFC	intermediate form of contract
IFC	International Finance Corporation (UN)
IFC 84	Intermediate Form of Building Contract 1984 edition (JCT)
IFC/FS	Fluctuations Supplement for use with IFC 84

IFC/SCS	Sectional Completion Supplement for use with IFC 84
IFE	Institute of Fire Engineers
IFGB	Institute of Foresters of Great Britain
IFIP	International Federation for Information Processing
IFireE	Institute of Fire Engineers
IFPI	International Federation of Phonogram and Videogram Producers
IFPRA	International Federation of Park and Recreation Administration
IFSA	Intumescent Fire Seals Association
IFYA	International Forum of Young Architects
IG	Ilford, Essex (postcode area)
IG	imperial gallon
IG	Institution of Geologists
IGADD	Inter-Governmental Authority on Drought and Development
IGasE, IGE	Institution of Gas Engineers
IGES	initial graphic exchange specification (computers)
IH	Institute of Hydrology
IHE	Institution of Highway Engineers
IHospE	Institute of Hospital Engineering
IHT	inheritance tax
IHT	Institution of Highways and Transportation
IHVE	Institution of Heating and Ventilating Engineers
IIA	industrial improvement area
IIASA	International Institute for Applied Systems Analysis
IIB	International Investment Bank (same membership as COMECON)
IIC	International Institute of Communications
IICHAW	International Institute for Conservation of Historic and Artistic Works
IIED	International Institute for Environment and Development
IInfSc	Institute of Information Scientists
IIR	isobutene-isoprene rubber
IIRSM	International Institute of Risk and Safety Management
IL	invert level
ILA	Institute of Landscape Architects (now LI)

ILAM	Institute of Leisure and Amenity Management	IMRA	Industrial Marketing Research Association
ILE	Institution of Lighting Engineers	IMS	Institute of Management Services
ILEA	Inner London Education Authority	IMS	Institute of Manpower Studies
ILGA	Institute of Local Government Administrators (now merged with ICSA)	IMSO	Institute of Municipal Safety Officers
		IMunE	Institution of Municipal Engineers
ILI	Infonorme – London Information (= London Information (Rowse Muir) Ltd, standards supply company)	in	inch, inches
		In	indium (chemical element)
		IN	intelligent network (computers)
		inc, incl	including
ILO	International Labour Organisation (UN)	Inc	incorporated
ILR	International Law Reports	INDECS	interactive design of control systems (computers)
IM	polyisobutene (rubber)	inf	infinity
IMAGE	Interface Maintenance Advisory Group, Europe (commercial carpet tile service company)	inf, info	information
		INFCO	ISO Standing Committee for the Study of Scientific and Technical Information on Standardisation
IMBM	Institute of Maintenance and Building Management	infra dig	infra dignitatem (Lat: beneath one's dignity)
IMC	Institute of Management Consultants	Ing	Ingénieur (engineer)
IMC	Institute of Measurement and Control	IN/SCa	Articles of Agreement for Domestic Contracts under IFC 84 (BEC)
IMCIG	Institute of Marketing, Construction Industry Group	IN/SCc	Conditions for Domestic Contracts under IFC 84 (BEC)
IMCO	International Maritime Consultative Organisation (UN)	INSIS	Community Inter-Institutional Information System (EC)
IME	Institution of Municipal Engineers	inst	instant, of this month
IMEA	Incorporated Municipal Electrical Association	Inst	institute, institution
		InstCES	Institution of Civil Engineering Surveyors
IMechE	Institution of Mechanical Engineers	InstMC	Institute of Measurement and Control
IMF	International Metalworkers Federation	INSTRAW	International Research and Training Institute for the Advancement of Women (UN)
IMF	International Monetary Fund (UN)		
IMGTE	Institution of Mechanical and General Technician Engineers	insul	insulation
		int	interior, internal
IMH	Institute of Materials Handling	int	international
IMI	Imperial Metals Industries	INTA	International Association for the Development and Management of Existing and New Towns (Fr: AIVN)
IMinE	Institution of Mining Engineers		
IMM	Institute of Materials Management		
IMM	Institution of Minerals and Metals	Intel	integrated electronics (American microcomputer manufacturer)
IMM	Institution of Mining and Metallurgy	INTELSAT	International Telecommunications Satellite Consortium
IMM	sieve number system (Institution of Minerals and Metals)		
		Interpave	Concrete Block Paving Association
IMO	International Maritime Organisation (UN)	IntLR	International Law Reports
IMP	Integrated Mediterranean Programmes	INucE	Institution of Nuclear Engineers
IMR	Institute for Market Research	inv	invert, invert level

I/O	input and output
IO	*Inside Out* (architectural periodical)
IO	intelligence officer
Io	ionium (old name for isotope thorium-230, a product of uranium decay)
IOA	Institute of Acoustics
IoAAS	Institute of Advanced Architectural Studies (University of York)
IOB	Institute of Building (now CIOB)
IOBM	Institute of Builders Merchants
IOC	Institute of Carpenters
IOCU	International Organisation of Consumers Unions (ICOU)
IOD	Institute of Directors
IOE	Institute of Energy
IOE	Institute of Offshore Engineering
IOF	Institute of Fuel
IOH	Institute of Horticulture
IOH	Institute of Housing
IOLM	International Organisation for Legal Metrology (= OIML)
IOM	Institute of Metals
IOM	Institute of Occupational Medicine (Edinburgh)
IOM	Isle of Man (BS code)
IOP	Institute of Plumbing
IOR	Institute for Operational Research
IOR	Institute of Roofing
IOS	Institute of Oceanographic Sciences
IOS	Isles of Scilly (BS code)
IOSH	Institution of Occupational Safety and Health
IoT	Institute of Transport
IoTA	Institute of Transport Administrators
IOU	I owe you
IoW	Isle of Wight
IOW	Isle of Wight (BS county code)
IP	information provider
IP	Institute of Petroleum
IP	Institute of Physics
IPA	International Phonetic Alphabet
IPA	International Playground Association
IPC	Inspectorate of Pollution Control
IPC	integrated pollution control
IPCC	Inter-governmental Panel on Climate Change
IPCS	Institution of Professional Civil Servants
IPE	see IPlantE

IPHE	Institution of Public Health Engineers
IPlantE	Institution of Plant Engineers
IPM	Institute of Personnel Management
IPM	Integrated Pest Management (EC)
IPMS	Institution of Professionals, Managers and Specialists (Civil Service union)
IPQ	Institute Portugès de Qualidada (Portugese Standards Institute)
IPR	Institute of Public Relations
IPRA	Institute of Park and Recreation Administration
IPS	Institute of Purchasing and Supply
IPU	Inter-Parliamentary Union
IPUG	IBM PC User Group (computers)
IQ	intelligence quotient
IQ	internal quality (bricks – pre-1985 designation)
IQA	Institute of Quality Assurance
IQS	Institute of Quantity Surveyors (amalgamated with RICS)
IR	industrial relations
IR	infra-red
IR	Inland Revenue
Ir	iridium (chemical element)
Ir	Irish
IR	*Irish Reports* (law reports)
IR	isoprene rubber (synthetic)
IRA	Institute of Registered Architects (merged with FAS in 1974)
IRB	Informationszentrum RAUM und BAU der Fraunhofer Gesellschaft (Information Centre for Regional Planning and Building Construction of the Fraunhofer Society – West Germany)
Irdac	Industrial Research and Development Advisory Committee (EC)
IRDS	information resource dictionary system (computers)
IRF	International Road Federation
IRIS	Industrial Research Information Services
IRM	Institute of Recreation Management
IRPTC	International Register of Potentially Toxic Chemicals (UNEP)
IRR	infra-red reflective
IRR	internal rate of return

IRRD	International Road Research Database (TRRL)	ISV	International Scientific Vocabulary
irreg	irregular	ISVA	Incorporated Society of Valuers and Auctioneers
IRSO	Institute of Road Safety Officers	ISVR	Institute of Sound and Vibration Research (Southampton University)
IRTE	Institute of Road Transport Engineers		
IS	Industrial Society	IT	income tax
IS	input system (computers)	IT	information technology
Is	island	IT	Institute of Technology
ISALPA	Incorporated Society of Auctioneers and Landed Property Agents	IT	intercepting trap
		It	Italian
		it	italic
ISBN	international standard book number	ITA	Institute of Transport Administration
ISCA	International Standards Steering Committee for Consumer Affairs	ITAP	Information Technology Advisory Panel
ISCE	Institute of Sound and Communications Engineers	ITB	industry training board
		ITB	Irish Tourist Board
ISDN	integrated services digital network (telecommunications)	ITC	International Tin Council
		ITDG	Intermediate Technology Development Group
ISE	Institution of Structural Engineers	ITE	Institute of Terrestrial Ecology (NERC)
ISE	International Stock Exchange	ITE	Institution of Electrical and Electronics Technician Engineers
ISES	International Solar Energy Society		
ISHSAA	Institute of Shops, Health and Safety Acts Administration (now ISPP)	ITER	International Thermonuclear Experimental Reactor (EC)
		ITF	International Transport Federation
ISIC	International Standard Industrial Classification	ITPA	International Truss Plate Association
ISL	internally-silvered lamp	ITR	*Industrial Tribunal Reports*
ISME	Institute of Sheet Metal Engineering	ITS	Information Thru Speech (American microcomputer for the blind, with voice synthesiser and interconnected brailler)
ISO	International Organisation for Standardisation		
iso	isometric projection		
ISPE	Institute of Swimming Pool Engineers	ITS	Institute for Transport Studies
ISPP	Institute of Safety and Public Protection (formerly ISHSAA)	ITSA	Institute of Trading Standards Administrators
ISSMFE	International Society for Soil Mechanics and Foundation Engineering	ITTA	independent taxation with transferable allowance
		ITTO	International Tropical Timber Organisation
ISSN	international standard serial number	ITTTF	Information Technology and Telecommunications Task Force (EC)
IST	institute of science and technology	ITU	intensive therapy unit
ISTC	Institute of Scientific and Technical Communicators	ITU	International Telecommunications Union (UN)
ISTC	Iron and Steel Trades Confederation	ITY	Information Technology Year (1982)
IStructE	Institution of Structural Engineers	IUA	inner urban area (DOE)
ISTT	International Society for Trenchless Technology	IUA	International Union of Architects (better known as the UIA)

IUBC	International Union of Building Centres (= UICB)	IWEM	Institution of Water and Environmental Management
IUCN	International Union for the Conservation of Nature and Natural Resources	IWES	Institution of Water Engineers and Scientists
IUG	Intergraph User Group (computers)	IWHM	Institution of Works and Highways Management
IULA	International Union of Local Authorities	IWHTE	Institution of Works and Highways Technician Engineers
IUTEP	International Urban Technology Exchange Programme	IWM	Institute of Wastes Management
		IWPC	Institution of Water Pollution Control
IV	Inverness (postcode area)	IWS	Industrial Water Society
		IWSA	International Water Supply Association
		IWSc	Institute of Wood Science
IWA	Inland Waterways Association	IWSOM	Institute of Practitioners in Work Study, Organisation and Methods
IWAAC	Inland Waterways Amenity Advisory Council	IWSP	Institute of Work Study Practitioners
IWandD	Inland Waterways and Docks		

J

J	joule (unit of work, energy, quantity of heat)	JCT	Joint Contracts Tribunal
		Jct	junction
J	Judge, Justice	JCT 63	JCT Standard Form of Building Contract 1963 edition
J	Waterproofing (Common Arrangement)	JCT 80	JCT Standard Form of Building Contract 1980 edition
JACLA	Joint Airports Committee of Local Authorities	JESI	Joint European Standards Institution (CEN/CENELEC)
JACLAP	Joint Advisory Committee on Local Authority Purchasing (now merged with LAMSAC)	JET	Joint European Torus (EC nuclear energy programme)
Jan	January	JETRO	Japan External Trade Organisation
JATCA	Joinery and Timber Construction Association	JG	junior girls (school)
JB	junior boys (school)	JIB	Joint Industry Board for the Electrical Contracting Industry
JCAR	Joint Committee for Architectural Registration	JInstE	Junior Institution of Engineers
JCB	proprietary name for excavators etc (from Joseph Cyril Bamford)	JIT	just in time (industrial philosophy)
JCBL	Joint Committee on Building Legislation	JJJ	Johnson Jackson Jeff (project control consultants)
JCL	job control language (computers)		
JCLI	Joint Council for Landscape Industries	JLO	Junior Liaison Organisation (of architects, quantity surveyors, builders, planners and engineers)
JCLMTU	Joint Committee of Light Metal Trades Unions		
JCP	Job Creation Programme	JMI	junior mixed infants (school)

jn	junction	JSA	Japanese Standards Association
jnd	just noticeable difference	jst	joist
Jnr	junior	JSY	Jersey, Channel Islands (BS code)
jnt	joint		
		jt	joint
JOULE	Joint Opportunities for Unconverted or Long Term Energy Supply (EC)	JTC	joint technical committee (ISO and IEC)
		JTC1	JTC on information technology standards activities
JP	jet propulsion		
JP	Justice of the Peace	JTCA	see JATCA
JP	*Justice of the Peace Reports* (law reports)	JTM	job transfer and manipulation (computers)
JPEL	*Journal of Planning and Environment Law* (periodical and law reports)	Jul	July
		Jun	June
JPS	joint parliamentary secretary	jun	junior
		Junc	junction
Jr	junior		
JRC	Joint Research Centre (EC)	JVT	joint venture tendering

K

k	conductivity (of a material)	KC	King's Counsel
k	constant (mathematics)	kcal	kilocalorie (obsolete – superseded by kilojoule)
K	kalium (potassium – chemical element)		
		KCB	Knight Commander of the Bath
k	kelvin (unit of thermodynamic temperature – SI basic unit)	kc/s	kilocycles per second
		KCVO	Knight Commander of the Royal Victorian Order
K	K factor (gamma ray dose rate of a source)		
K	kilobyte	KEHFL	King Edward's Hospital Fund for London
k	kilo (multiple prefix: 10^3 or 1000)		
K	kilo (multiple prefix for computer storage locations: 2^{10} or 1024)	KEN	Kent (BS county code)
		K factor	maximum price rise above rate of inflation permitted for a water company
K	kitchen		
K	Linings/Sheathing/Dry partitioning (Common Arrangement)	KFC	King's Fund Centre
		kg	kilogram (unit of mass – SI basic unit)
KA	Kilmarnock, Ayrshire (postcode area)		
		KG	Knight of the Garter
KB	kilobyte	KG	kommandit gesellschaft (limited partnership)
KB	King's Bench (division of High Court)		
KB	*Kings's Bench* (law reports)	KGB	Komitet Gossudarstvennoi Bezopastnosti (USSR Committee of State Security – secret police)
KBE	Knight Commander of the British Empire		
kbps	kilobits per second	kHz	kilohertz
KBTG	Keep Britain Tidy Group		
		kilo	kilogram
kc	kilocycle	kip	1000 lb

KK	kaien kaisha (limited company)		kt	kilotonne
			KT	Kingston-upon-Thames, Surrey (postcode area)
km	kilometre			
			Kt	knight
kn	knot (nautical)			
			kV	kilovolt
KO	knock-out		k-value	thermal conductivity
kph	kilometres per hour			
KPS	knot, prime and stop		kW	kilowatt
			KW	Kirkwall, Orkney (postcode area)
Kr	krypton (chemical element)		kWh	kilowatt hour
kT	kiloton		KY	Kirkcaldy, Fife (postcode area)

L

L	50 (Roman numeral)		LAIA	Latin American Integration Association (= ALADI)
L	lake			
L	lambert (unit of luminance; generally superseded by candela per unit area)		LAIG	Library Association Information Group
			LAMS	London Association of Master Stonemasons
L	Latin			
L	learner		LAMSAC	Local Authorities Management Services and Computer Committee
L	left			
L	length			
L	libra (Lat: pound – currency)		LAMSJC	London Area Mobility Scheme Joint Committee
l	litre (= dm^3)			
L	Liverpool (postcode area)		LAMUG	Local Authority Micro-Computer User Group
L	location drawing			
L	Windows/Doors/Stairs (Common Arrangement)		LAN	Lancashire (BS county code)
			LAN	local area network (computers)
L_{10}	dB(A) level exceeded for 10% of the time		l&h	lime and hair
			l&m	labour and materials
			l&p	lath and plaster
L_{10}(18 hour), $L_{10,18h}$			l&r	level and ram
	average of L_{10} between 0600 and 2400 hours		LANTAC	Local Authority National Type Approval Confederation
LA	Lancaster (postcode area)		LAS	Land Agents Society
La	lanthanum (chemical element)		LAS	League of Arab States (The Arab League)
LA	leaf applied (herbicide)			
LA	Library Association		LAS	Liverpool Architectural Society (RIBA branch)
LA	local authority			
lab	labour, labourer		LASCO	Local Authority Support Company
LABC	Local Authority Building Control			
LAC	leaf applied contact (herbicide)		laser	light amplification by stimulated emission of radiation
LACBTS	see LACOTS			
LACOTS	Local Authorities Co-ordinating Body on Trading Standards		LASI	Licentiate of the Architects and Surveyors Institute
LACSAB	Local Authorities Conditions of Service Advisory Board		Lat	Latin
			lat	latitude

LAT	leaf applied translocated or systemic (herbicide)
LATA	London Amenity and Transport Association
LAWAQ	local authorities with approximate quantities (version of SFBC)
LAWOQ	local authorities without quantities (version of SFBC)
LAWQ	local authorities with quantities (version of SFBC)
L_{AX}	single event noise exposure level
LAXQ	local authorities without quantities (version of SFBC)
LB	lavatory basin
lb	*libra* (Lat: pound – weight)
LBA	London Boroughs Association (Conservative)
LBA	London Building Act
LBC	London borough council
LBEMG	London Boroughs Energy Management Group
LBGU	London Boroughs Grants Unit
LBTC	London Boroughs Transport Committee
LBVGU	London Boroughs Voluntary Grant Unit
LC, lc	lower case (print)
LCA	Lead Contractors Association
LCACM	Liaison Committee of Architects of the Common Market
LCC	London County Council (1888-1965)
LCCI	London Chamber of Commerce and Industry
LCD	liquid crystal display
lcd	lowest common denominator
LCJ	Lord Chief Justice
lcm	lowest common multiple
LCMA	Lighting Column Manufacturers Association
LD	Llandrindod Wells, Powys (postcode area)
Ld	Lord
LDA	Lead Development Association
LDC	Leeds Development Corporation
LDC	Livingstone Development Corporation
LDCs	Least Developed Countries (UN list)
LDDC	London Docklands Development Corporation
LDEC	Land Decade Educational Council
LDPE	low density polyethylene

LDSA	London District Surveyors Association
LDT	land development tax
LDY	Londonderry, Northern Ireland (BS code)
LE	Leicester (postcode area)
LEA	local education authority
LEAAP	local environmental audit and action plan (Camden LBC)
LEB	London Electricity Board
LEC	Leicestershire (BS county code)
LEC	London Ecology Centre
LECA	light expanded clay aggregate
LECC	London Electricity Consultative Council
LECHRA	housing subsidy computer (DOE)
LED	light emitting diode
LEDU	Local Enterprise Development Unit (Northern Ireland)
LEEA	Lifting Equipment Engineers Association
LEEC	London Environmental Economics Centre
LEEG	London Environment and Energy Group (RIBA, CIBSE and RICS)
len	length
LEntA	London Enterprise Agency
LEO	Lyons Electronic Office (1951 – first office computer)
L_{eq}	equivalent continuous sound level
LET	London and Edinburgh Trust
LETIS	LET Information Services
levs	levels
LF	low frequency
LFA	less-favoured area (EC)
LFB	London Fire Brigade
LFCDA	London Fire and Civil Defence Authority
LFI	Landscape Filing Index
LFS	Licentiate of the Faculty of Architects and Surveyors
LGBCE	Local Government Boundary Commission for England
LGBCS	Local Government Boundary Commission for Scotland
LGBCW	Local Government Boundary Commission for Wales
LGC	Laboratory of the Government Chemist
LGFA	Lattice Girder Floor Association
LGIU	Local Government Information Unit
LGR	Local Government Reports (law reports)

69

LH	left hand
LHA	local health authority
LHB	Lanarkshire Health Board
LHB	Lothian Health Board
LHC	London Housing Consortium
LHS	left-hand side
LHU	London Housing Unit
LI	Landscape Institute (formerly ILA)
Li	lithium (chemical element)
Lidar	light detection and ranging (environment research)
LIF	Lighting Industry Federation
LIFO	last in first out (electronic mail)
LIN	Lincolnshire (BS county code)
lin	linear
LISP	list processing language (computers)
LJ	Lord Justice
LJCP	*Law Journal Common Pleas* (law reports)
LJKB	*Law Journal King's Bench* (law reports)
LJQB	*Law Journal Queen's Bench* (law reports)
LL	Llandudno (postcode area)
LLDPE	linear low density polyethylene
Lloyds Rep	*Lloyds Law Reports*
lm	lumen (unit of luminous flux)
LME	low density medium board – extra density
LMGSC	London and Metropolitan Government Staff Commission
LMN	low density medium board – normal density
LMPA	London Master Plasterers Association
LMV	Limavady, Northern Ireland (BS code)
LN	Lincoln (postcode area)
LNG	liquified natural gas
lo	linseed oil
LOA	leave of absence
loc cit	*loco citato* (Lat: in the place cited)
L of C	lines of communication
log	logarithm
Lomé	Lomé Convention (see ACP)
long	longitude
LONTA	Intermediate Technology Voluntary Development Agency (UN)

LOX	liquid oxygen
lp	large pipe
£p	pounds and pence
LPA	local planning authority
LPAC	London Planning Advisory Committee
LPAS	London Planning Aid Service (TCPA) (now PAL)
LPC	less prosperous country (EC)
LPC	Loss Prevention Council
LPCTC	Loss Prevention Council Technical Centre
LPG	liquified petroleum gas
LPGITA	Liquid Petroleum Gas Industry Technical Association (UK)
lpi	lines per inch
lpm	lines per minute
L_{PN}	perceived noise level
LPU	low pay unit
Lr	lawrencium (chemical element)
LR	*The Law Reports*
LR	living room
LR	LLoyds Register
LRA	legionella rapid assay (test)
LRB	London Residual Body
LRC	London Regeneration Consortium
LRC	London Research Centre
LRIBA	Licentiate of the RIBA (pre-1971)
LRN	Larne, Northern Ireland (BS code)
LRQA	Lloyd's Register Quality Assurance
LRSA	Leicestershire and Rutland Society of Architects (RIBA branch)
LRT	London Regional Transport
LRTL	Light Railway Transport League
LS	Leeds (postcode area)
LS	loudspeaker (sound amplifier)
LSA	Lead Sheet Association
LSA	Leeds Society of Architects (RIBA branch)
LSA	Lincolnshire Society of Architects (RIBA branch)
LSB	Lisburn, Northern Ireland (BS code)
LSC	London Salvage Corps (fire)
LSD	labour-saving devices
LSD, £sd	pounds, shillings and pence
LSE	language symbolique d'enseignement (high level computer language)
LSE	London School of Economics

LSE	London Stock Exchange
LSI	large scale integration (computers)
LSPU	London Strategic Policy Unit
LSS	London Scientific Services
LT	Lands Tribunal
LT	*Law Times* (law reports)
LT	London Transport
LTB	London Tourist Board
LTB	London Transport Board (now LTE)
Ltd	limited (company)
LTE	London Transport Executive
ltg	lighting
LTN	Lothian Region, Scotland (BS code)
LTS	Lands Tribunal for Scotland
Lu	lutetium (chemical element)

LU	Luton (postcode area)
LUL	London Underground Limited
LUR	Lovell Urban Renewal
LV	luncheon voucher
LVC	local valuation court
LVRPA	Lee Valley Regional Park Authority
LVT	leasehold valuation tribunal
LVWC	Lee Valley Water Company
LW	long wave
LW	low water
LWR	light water reactor
LWRA	London Waste Regulatory Authority
LWSA	Lancaster and Westmorland Society of Architects (RIBA branch)
lx	lux (unit of illuminance)

M

M	1000 (Roman numeral)
M̄	1,000,000 (Roman numeral)
M	Mach number (see Ma)
M	maisonette
m	male, masculine
M	Manchester (postcode area)
M	mean line (a system of expressing surface flatness)
M	megabyte
M	mega (multiple prefix: 10^6 or 1 000 000; but 2^{20} or 1 048 576 in computer storage locations)
M	member
M	men
m	metre (unit of length – SI basic unit)
m	million
m	milli (submultiple prefix: 10^{-3})
m	minute
M	module of 100 mm
M	Monday
M	motorway
M	Surface finishes (Common Arrangement)
M1	total money supply in most liquid form

M2	M1 plus clearing bank and discount house deposits (not used since 1972)
M3	M1 plus assets liquifiable in the short term
M50, M75	machine grades (structural softwood classification groups)
Ma	Mach number (ratio of speed of object to speed of sound)
MA	Master of Arts
mA	milliampere
MA	Museums Association
MACE	Metropolitan Architectural Consortium for Education
MACEF	Mastic Asphalt Council and Employers Federation
MAFF	Ministry of Agriculture, Fisheries and Food
MAN	metropolitan area network (computers)
M&E	mechanical and electrical engineers/engineering/services
Manweb	Merseyside and North Wales Electricity Board (formerly Manchester ...)
MAP	manufacturing automation profile (computers)

MAP	Microprocessor Application Project (DTI)
MAPCON	MAP Consultants (part of MAP scheme)
MAQ	married airmen's quarters
Mar	March
MARC	Manufacturers Association of Radiators and Convectors
MArch	Master of Architecture
MARCOGAZ	Union of Gas Industries of Common Market Countries
MARI	Microelectronics Application Research Institute
MARS	Modern Architectural Research
masc	masculine
MASER	microwave amplification by stimulated emission of radiation
MASI	Member of the Architects and Surveyors Institute
MAST	Marine Science and Technology
math	mathematics, mathematical
MATSA	Managerial, Administrative, Technical and Supervisory Association (GMWU non-manual workers section)
MA(UrbDes)	Master of Arts in Urban Design
max	maximum
Mb	megabyte
mb	millibar
MBC	metropolitan borough council
MBE	Member of the British Empire
MBF, MBFA, MBF de luxe	high pressure mercury discharge (fluorescent) lamps
MBFT/MBTF	high pressure mercury tungsten discharge (blended) lamps
mbH	mit beschränkter haftung (with limited liability)
MBI, MBIF, MBIL, MBIR	high pressure mercury discharge (metal halide) lamps
MBIAT	Member of the British Institute of Architectural Technicians
MBIM	Member of the British Institute of Management
mbps	megabits per second (computers)
m/c	machine
MC	main contractor
MC	management contract
MC	management contractor
MC	master of ceremonies
MC	Military Cross
MC 87	Management Contract 1987 edition (JCT)
MCA	Management Consultancies Association

MCA	micro channel architecture (IBM technology – computers)
MCA	monetary compensation amount (EC)
MCAC	Management and Co-ordination Advisory Committees (EC)
MCB	miniature circuit breaker
MCD	Master of Civic Design
MCF, MCFA, MCFE, MCFR	low pressure mercury discharge lamps
MCIOB	Member of the Chartered Institute of Building
Mc/s	megacycles per second
MCSD	Member of the Chartered Society of Designers
MD	managing director
Md	mendelevium (chemical element)
MDA	monochrome display adaptor
MDC	Merseyside Development Corporation
MDF	medium density fibreboard
ME	materials engineering
ME	mechanical and electrical engineers/engineering/services
ME	mechanical engineer
ME	Medway (postcode area)
ME	Middle East
meas sep	measured separately
MEB	Midlands Electricity Board
mech	mechanics, mechanical
med	medium
Mem	member
memo	memorandum
MENTOR	a computer-based learning system
MEP	Manuals of Engineering Practice (ASCE)
MEP	Member of the European Parliament
MERB	Mechanical Engineering Research Board
met	metal
Met	Meteorological Office
met	meteorology, meteorological
Met	metropolitan
METHOD	Consortium of Method Building
MeV	mega electron volts
Mezz	mezzanine
MF	medium frequency
MF	melamine, melamine formaldehyde
MFA	Multi-fibre Agreement (under GATT)

MfL	Movement for London
MFQ	silicone rubber having methyl and fluorine substituent groups on the polymer chain
MFT	Magherafelt, Northern Ireland (BS code)
Mg	magnesium (chemical element)
mg	make good
mg	milligram
MGC	Museums and Galleries Commission
MGD	making good defects
MGM	Mid Glamorgan (BS county code)
MGS	machine general structural (structural softwood classification)
MH	manhole
mH	millihenry (inductance – see H)
MHD	magnetohydrodynamic (electricity generating system)
MHF	medium high frequency
MHLG	Ministry of Housing and Local Government (1951–1970)
MHS	message handling system (same as electronic mail)
MHTGR	modular high temperature gas-cooled reactor
MHW	mean high water (in England and Wales)
MHWS	mean high water springs (in Scotland)
MHz	megahertz
MI	Materials Information (IOM)
mi	mitre
MIAA	Member Architect of the Incorporated Association of Architects and Surveyors
MIAA&S	Member Architect and Surveyor of the Incorporated Association of Architects and Surveyors
MIAS	Member Surveyor of the Incorporated Association of Architects and Surveyors
MICC	mineral insulated copper covered (cable)
MICE	Member of the Institute of Civil Engineers
MICR	magnetic ink character recognition
micron	unit of length (= 10^{-6} m – symbol μ) (term superseded by 'micrometre' – symbol μm)
micron	unit of pressure (= 10^{-6} m of mercury)
MIEE	Member of the Institution of Electrical Engineers
MIERE	Member of the Institute of Electronic and Radio Engineers
mil	angular: one thousandth of a right angle (USA military in WW2), or one thousanth of a radian
mil	circular: area of circle of one thousandth of an inch diameter
mil	length: one thousandth of an inch
mil	volume: millilitre (ml) (used mainly in pharmacy)
Mil Spec	military specification (USA)
MIMechE	Member of the Institution of Mechanical Engineers
MIMunE	Member of the Institution of Municipal Engineers
min	minimum
Min	ministry
min	minute
MInstP	Member of the Institute of Physics
MIPS	million instructions per second
MIRA	Member of the Institute of Registered Architects
MIRAGE	Migration of Radio-isotopes in the Geosphere (radioactive waste programme)
MIRAS	mortgage interest relief at source
MIS	management information system
mis	mitres
misc	miscellaneous
MISP	microelectronics industry support programme
MIStructE	Member of the Institution of Structural Engineers
MIT	Massachusetts Institute of Technology
Mk	mark (monetary unit of Germany)
MK	Milton Keynes
MK	Milton Keynes (postcode area)
MKDC	Milton Keynes Development Corporation
MKS	metre kilogram second (system of units)
MKWC	Mid Kent Water Company
ml	millilitre
ML	moderately frost resistant and with low soluble salt content (bricks)
ML	Motherwell, Lanarkshire (postcode area)
mld	moulded
MLR	minimum lending rate

MLURI	Macaulay Land Use Research Institute
MLW	mean low water (in England and Wales)
MLWS	mean low water springs (in Scotland)
MM	master mason
mm	millimetre
mm	*mutatis mutandis* (Lat: the necessary changes having been made)
MMC	Monopolies and Mergers Commission
mmf	magnetomotive force
mmHg	millimetres of mercury
MMI	man machine interface
MMMF	man-made mineral fibre
mmsf	machine made sand faced
Mn	manganese (chemical element)
MN	moderately frost resistant and with normal soluble salt content (bricks)
MO	medical officer
MO	Meteorological Office
MO	*modus operandi* (Lat: method of operation)
Mo	molybdenum (chemical element)
mo	moment (slang)
mo	moulded
MOAT	method of assessment and testing (BBA)
MoD	Ministry of Defence
mod cons	modern conveniences
modem	modulator/demodulator
MODUSSE	Association of Manufacturers of Domestic Unvented Supply Systems Equipment
MOEH	medical officer for environmental health
MOHLG, MOHLOG	Ministry of Housing and Local Government (1951–1970)
mol	mole (unit of amount of substance – SI basic unit)
MOL	Museum of London
Mon	Monday
MOQ	married officers' quarters
MOS	metal oxide semiconductor (computers)
MOSFET	MOS field effect transistor (computers)
MOTIS	message-orientated text interchange system (computers)
MOTT	Men of the Trees

mouse	minimal orbital unmanned satellite of the earth
MOW	Ministry of Works (1943–1962)
mp	melting point
MP	Member of Parliament
MPA	Mortar Producers Association
MPA	multi-user project access (t^2 Solutions software)
MPBB	maximum permissible body burden (plutonium contamination)
MPBW	Ministry of Public Buildings and Works (1962–1970)
MPC	multi-project chip (Australian silicon chip – computers)
MPCN	Mercury Personal Communications Networks
MPF	melamine phenol formaldehyde
mpg	miles per gallon
MPGA	Metropolitan Public Gardens Association
mph	miles per hour
MP/M	a control program (multi-user version of CP/M)
MPP	maternity pay period
MPQ	silicone rubber having methyl and phenyl substituent groups on the polymer chain
mps	metres per second
MPU	microprocessor unit
MPVQ	silicone rubber having methyl, phenyl and vinyl substituent groups on the polymer chain
MQ	married quarters
MQ	silicone rubber having only methyl substituent groups on the polymer chain; eg dimethyl polysiloxane
MR	moisture-resistant (plywood)
M_r	moment of resistance
MRA	multiple regression analysis
MRC	Medical Research Council
MRDA	Metal Roof Deck Association
MRE	Microbiological Research Establishment
MRHA	Mersey Regional Health Authority
MRP	manufacturer's recommended price
MRPRA	Malaysian Rubber Producers Research Association
MRTPI	Member of the Royal Town Planning Institute
MRU	Market Research Unit (RIBA)

MS	Mackintosh School (Glasgow)	MTC 89	Measured Term Contract 1989 edition (JCT)
MS	Manpower Society		
MS	manuscript	MTCA	Ministry of Transport and Civil Aviation (1953–1959)
ms	measured separately		
MS	Member States of the EC	MTCP	Ministry of Town and Country Planning (1942–1951)
MS	Metals Society		
MS	Microsoft	MTFA	Medium-term Financial Assistance (EMS)
MS	mild steel		
MSA	Manchester Society of Architects (RIBA branch)	MTFS	medium-term financial strategy
		MTIA	see Wolfson
MSAAT	Member of the Society of Architectural and Allied Technicians (now MBIAT)	MTM	methods-time measurement (time and motion study)
		MTN	Main Telecommunications Network (UN: WMO)
MSC	Manpower Services Commission (now Training Agency)	MTPI	Member of the Town Planning Institute (now MRTPI)
MSc	Master of Science	MTTA	Machine Tool Trades Association
MSD	Machinery Safety Directive (EC)	MTTR	mean time to repair
msd	measured		
MS-DOS	Microsoft disk operating system (computers)	MUF	materials unaccounted for (atomic energy)
msec	millisecond	MUG	Moss User Group (computers)
MSF	Manufacturing Science Finance (union)	mull	mullion
		Mun	municipal
MSF	Multiple Shops Federation	MuPVC	modified unplasticised PVC
MSI	medium-scale integration (computers)		
MSL	mean sea level	MV	market value
MSMA	Metal Sink Manufacturers Association	mV	millivolt
		MVQ	silicone rubber having methyl and vinyl substituent groups on the polymer chain
MSP	mild steel plate		
MSQ	married soldiers' quarters		
MSS	machine special structural (structural softwood classification)	MW	medium wave
		MW	megawatt
		mW	milliwatt
MSS	manuscripts	MW	minor works
MST	*Materials Science and Technology*	MW 68	Agreement for Minor Works 1968 edition (JCT)
MSWC	Mid Southern Water Company		
MSWC	Mid-Sussex Water Company	MW 80	Agreement for Minor Works 1980 edition (JCT)
MSX	a Japanese/American software and hardware standard (computers)		
		MWB	Metropolitan Water Board
MSY	Merseyside (BS county code)	MYB	*Municipal Year Book*
		MYBP	millions of years before the present
MT	megaton		
Mt	mount, mountain	MYL	Moyle, Northern Ireland (BS code)
MTBF	mean time between failures		
MTC	measured term contract		

N

N	Furniture/Equipment (Common Arrangement)	NALM	National Association of Lift Makers
N	London Northern (postcode area)	NAM	New Architectural Movement
n	nano (submultiple prefix: 10^{-9})	NAMAS	National Measurement Accreditation Service
N	neutron number	NAM/FR	Formula Rules for Named
N	newton (unit of force)		Subcontractor for use with IFC 84
N	nitrogen (chemical element)	NAMM	National Association of Master
N	norm (standard)		Masons
N	north	NAM/SC	Subcontract Conditions for
N	number of threads per inch or cm of screw		Named Subcontractor for use with IFC 84
n	number (standing for any number in mathematics)	NAM/T	Named Subcontractor Tender and Agreement for use with IFC 84
Na	natrium (sodium – chemical element)	NAND	not AND (a logic gate – computers)
Na	noise rating number (tolerance level related to background noise)	NAO	National Audit Office
		NAPC	National Association of Parish Councils
N/A	not applicable	NAPGC	National Association of Public Golf Courses
na	not available		
NAA	Norfolk Association of Architects (RIBA branch)	NAPH&MSC	National Association of Plumbing, Heating and Mechanical Services Contractors
NAA	Northern Architectural Association	NAS	National Association of Shopfitters
NAAB	National Architectural Accrediting Board (USA)	NAS	Noise Abatement Society
NAAPL	National Association of Aerial Photographic Libraries	NASA	National Aeronautics and Space Administration (USA)
NAB	National Advisory Body	NASA	National Architecture Students Association
NAC	National Agricultural Centre		
NAC	Noise Advisory Council	NASC	National Association of Scaffolding Contractors
NACCB	National Accreditation Council for Certification Bodies (DTI/BSI)	NASS	National Association of Steel Stockholders
NACLE	National Association of Chimney Lining Engineers	Nat	national
NACRT	National Agricultural Centre Rural Trust (housing charity)	NATFHE	National Association of Teachers in Further and Higher Education
NAEA	National Association of Estate Agents	NATLAS	National Testing Laboratory Accreditation Scheme (DTI)
NAFC	National Association of Formwork Contractors	NATO	North Atlantic Treaty Organisation
NAFO	National Association of Fire Officers	NATSOPA	National Society of Operative Printers, Graphical and Media Personnel
NAG	National Association of Groundsmen		
NAGRA	National Co-operative for the Storage of Radioactive Waste	NAV	net annual value
		NAWDC	National Association of Waste Disposal Contractors
NAHA	National Association of Health Authorities in England and Wales		
NALC	National Association of Local Councils	Nb	niobium (chemical element)
		NB	*nota bene* (Lat: mark well)
NALGO	National and Local Government Officers Association	NBA	National Brassfoundry Association (formerly NBAHMA)
NALIC	National Association of Loft Insulation Contractors	NBA	National Building Agency (defunct)

NBAHMA	National Building and Allied Hardware Manufacturers Association (now NBA)
NBCC	Northern Building Control Consortium
NBD	Nederlandse Bouw-Dokumentatie BV (Dutch Building Documentation Centre)
NBL	Northumberland (BS county code)
NBPI	National Board for Prices and Incomes
NBR	nitrile-butadiene rubber
NBS	National Building Specification
NBS	National Bureau of Standards (USA)
NC	National Certificate
NC	noise criteria
NCARB	National Council of Architectural Registration Boards (USA equivalent of ARCUK)
NCAT	National Centre for Alternative Technology
NCB	National Coal Board
NCBIC	Northern Counties Building Information Centre (Durham)
NCBMP	see BMP
NCC	National Computing Centre
NCC	National Consumer Council
NCC	Nature Conservancy Council
NCCC	National Craftsmen's Co-ordinating Committee (iron and steel industry)
NCE	*New Civil Engineer*
NCF	National Clayware Federation
NCG	National Contractors Group
NCH	National Campaign for the Homeless (SHELTER)
NCHA	Northern Consortium of Housing Authorities
NCI	New Community Instruments (Ortoli Fund) (EC)
NCIA	National Cavity Insulation Association
NCND	neither confirm nor deny
NCP	National Car Parks
NCPS	non-contributary pension scheme
NCR	nitrile-chloroprene rubber
NCRT	National College of Rubber Technology
NCSIIB	National Certification Scheme for In-service Inspection Bodies
NCT	National Chamber of Trade
NCTA	National Council for Technological Awards

NCVQ	National Council for Vocational Qualifications
Nd	neodymium (chemical element)
NDD	National Diploma in Design
NDN	North Down, Northern Ireland (BS code)
NDSA	Nottingham and Derby Society of Architects (RIBA branch)
NDT	National Diploma in the Science and Practice of Turf-culture and Sportsground Management
NDT	non-destructive testing
Ne	neon (chemical element)
NE	Network Energy
NE	Newcastle-upon-Tyne (postcode area)
NE	north-east
n/e	not exceeding
NE	Nuclear Electric
NEA	Nuclear Energy Agency (OECD)
NEB	National Enterprise Board
NEBCC	North East Building Control Consortium
NEC	National Exhibition Centre
nec	necessary
NECC	National Engineering Construction Committee
NECEA	National Engineering Construction Employers Association
necess	necessary
NEDC	National Economic Development Council ('Neddy')
NEDO	National Economic Development Office
NEEA	National Energy Efficiency Association
NEEB	North Eastern Electricity Board
NEF	National Energy Foundation
NEL	National Engineering Laboratory (DTI)
NELP	North East London Polytechnic (now PEL)
nem con	*nemine contradicente* (Lat: no-one against)
nem dis	*nemine dissentiente* (Lat: no-one dissenting)
NEQ	non-equivalence (a logic gate – computers)
NERC	Natural Environment Research Council
NERPB	North-East River Purification Board
NES	National Engineering Specification

NET	Next European Torus (see JET) (EC)
NETSA	North East Thames Society of Architects (RIBA branch)
NFBTE	National Federation of Building Trades Employers (now BEC)
NFC	National Fireplace Council
NFC	National Freight Corporation
NFCI	National Federation of Clay Industries
NFCMA	National Fireplace Council Manufacturers Association
NFCO	National Federation of Community Organisations
NFCU	National Federation of Construction Unions
NFDC	National Federation of Demolition Contractors
NFFO	Non-Fossil-Fuel Obligation
NFFTU	National Federation of Furniture Trade Unions
NFHA	National Federation of Housing Associations
NFHS	National Federation of Housing Societies
NFK	Norfolk (BS county code)
NFMSLCE	National Federation of Master Steeplejacks and Lightning Conductor Engineers
NFPC	National Federation of Plastering Contractors
NFPDC	National Federation of Painting and Decorating Contractors
NFRC	National Federation of Roofing Contractors
NFSA	National Fire Services Association
NFSE	National Federation of the Self-Employed
NFTMS	National Federation of Terrazzo and Mosaic Specialists
NFTU	National Federation of Trade Unions
NFU	National Farmers Union
NG	National Grid (OS)
NG	Nottingham (postcode area)
NGA	National Graphical Association
NGC	National Grid Company (electricity)
NGCC	National Gas Consumers Council
NGCF	National GRP Cladding Federation
NGO	non-governmental organisation
NGS	National Gardens Scheme
NGWC	Newcastle and Gateshead Water Company
NHBC	National House-Building Council (formerly NHBRC)
NHBCBCS	NHBC Building Control Services
NHBPM	National Housebuilders' and Plumbers' Merchants
NHBRA	National House Builders Registration Association
NHBRC	National House Builders Registration Council (now NHBC)
NHC	National Housing Consortium
NHEB	National Home Enlargement Bureau
NHEG	New Homes Environmental Group
NHF	National Housing Forum
NHIC	National Home Improvement Council
NHMF	National Heritage Memorial Fund
NHS	National Health Service
NHSSB	Northern Health and Social Services Board (Northern Ireland)
NHTPC	National Housing and Town Planning Council
NI	national insurance
Ni	nickel (chemical element)
NI	Northern Ireland
NI	*Northern Ireland Law Reports*
NIA	net internal area
NIC	National Incomes Commission
NIC	national insurance contribution
NIC	New Community instrument for borrowing and lending (EC)
NICEIC	National Inspection Council for Electrical Installation Contracting
NICGB	National Illumination Committee of Great Britain
NIDEX	Northern Interior Design Exhibition
NIES	Northern Ireland Electricity Service
NIESR	National Institute of Economic and Social Research
NIFES	National Industrial Fuel Efficiency Service
NIHE	Northern Ireland Housing Executive
NII	Nuclear Installations Inspectorate
NIMBY	not in my back yard
NIR	nitrile-isoprene rubber
NIS	national insurance surcharge (employer's contribution)
NJB(ESI)	National Joint Board (Electricity Supply Industry)
NJCBI	National Joint Council for the Building Industries

NJCC	National Joint Consultative Committee for Building
NJCCAT	National Joint Council for Civil Air Transport
NJCECI	National Joint Council for the Engineering Construction Industry
NJIC	National Joint Industrial Council
NJICHVDE	National Joint Industrial Council for Heating and Ventilating Domestic Engineers
NJUG	National Joint Utility Group
NKTF	North Kensington Task Force
NLA	net lettable area
NLJ	*New Law Journal* (law reports)
NLQ	near letter quality (printing)
NLS	National Library of Scotland
NLSA	North Lancashire Society of Architects (RIBA branch)
NLW	National Library of Wales
NMHC	National Materials Handling Centre
n.mile	nautical mile (average meridian length of 1 minute of latitude)
NMO	National Mobility Office (housing)
NMR	National Monuments Record (part of RCHME)
NMRW	National Monuments Record for Wales (part of RCAHMW)
NMTFA	National Master Tile Fixers Association
NN	Northampton (postcode area)
NNDR	National Non-Domestic Rate (= uniform business rate)
NNDTC	National Non-destructive Testing Centre
NNE	north-north-east
NNI	Nederlandse Normalisatie Instituut (Dutch Standardisation Institution)
NNI	noise and number index (assessment of aircraft noise)
NNP	net national product
NNW	north-north-west
No	nobelium (chemical element)
no	number
nol pros	*nolle prosequi* (Lat: to refuse to pursue, stay of legal proceedings)
nom	nominal
non seq	*non sequitur* (Lat: it does not follow)

non-U	not upper-class
NOP	National Opinion Poll
NOR	not OR (a logic gate – computers)
Norw	Norway, Norwegian
NORWEB	North Western Electricity Board
nos	numbers
NOT	a logic gate (computers)
Nov	November
NP	National Power
Np	neptunium (chemical element)
np	new paragraph
NP	Newport, Gwent (postcode area)
NPBA	National Prefabricated Building Association
NPC	National Power Company
NPFA	National Playing Fields Association
NPKA	National Paving and Kerb Association
NPL	National Physical Laboratory (DTI)
NPMSC	National Professional and Management Staffs Council (TUC)
np or d	no place or date
NPT	normal pressure and temperature
NPV	net present value
NQIC	National Quality Information Centre
NR	natural rubber, isoprene rubber (natural)
nr	near
NR	noise rating
NR	Norwich (postcode area)
NRA	National Rivers Authority
NRAAC	National River Authority Advisory Committee
NRCA	Northern Region Councils Association
NRDC	National Research Development Corporation
NRPB	National Radiological Protection Board
NRR	Natural Resources Research
NRV	net realisable value
NRWB	National Register of Warranted Builders (FMB)
ns	nanosecond
Ns	nimbostratus (cloud classification)
NSA	Northamptonshire Society of Architects (RIBA branch)
NSAC	Nuclear Safety Advisory Committee

NSAI	National Standards Authority of Ireland
NSALG	National Society of Allotment and Leisure Gardeners
NSB	National Savings Bank
NSC	nominated subcontract/subcontractor
NSC/1	Nominated Subcontract Tender for use with JCT 80 – basic method
NSC/1a	Nominated Subcontract Tender for use with JCT 80 – alternative method
NSC/2	Nominated Subcontract Agreement for use with JCT 80 – basic method
NCS/2a	Nominated Subcontract Agreement for use with JCT 80 – alternative method
NSC/3	Nominated Subcontract Nomination for use with JCT 80 – basic method
NSC/3a	Nominated Subcontract Nomination for use with JCT 80 – alternative method
NSC/4	Nominated Subcontract for use with JCT 80 – basic method
NSC/4a	Nominated Subcontract for use with JCT 80 – alternative method
NSCA	National Society for Clean Air
NSCA:FBD	North of Scotland College of Agriculture: Farm Buildings Division
NSCIA	National Supervisory Council for Intruder Alarms
NSECC	North of Scotland Electricity Consultative Council
NSHEB	North of Scotland Hydro-Electric Board
NSMM	National Society of Metal Mechanics
NSQA	Natural Slate Quarries Association
NSR	National Schedule of Rates (BEC)
NSSA	North Staffordshire Society of Architects (RIBA branch)
NSSSBC	National Structural Steelwork Specification for Building Construction (BCSA)
NSWC	North Surrey Water Company
NSY	New Scotland Yard
NT	National Theatre
NT	National Trust for Places of Historic Interest or Natural Beauty
NT	new town
NT	new town development corporation
nt	nit (MKS unit of luminance)
NTA	national training award
NTA	Newtownabbey, Northern Ireland (BS code)
NTH	Northamptonshire (BS county code)
NTIS	National Technical Information Service (USA)
NTP	net trading profit
NTP	normal temperature and pressure
NTS	National Trust for Scotland
NTS	not to scale
NTT	Nottinghamshire (BS county code)
NUAAW	National Union of Agricultural and Allied Workers
NUB	National Union of Blastfurnacemen, Ore Miners, Coke Workers and Kindred Trades
NUDAGMW	National Union of Domestic Appliances and General Metal Workers
NUI	network user identifier (computers)
NUJ	National Union of Journalists
NULMW	National Union of Lock and Metal Workers
NUM	National Union of Mineworkers
NUPE	National Union of Public Employees
NURC	National Union of Research Councils
NUS	National Utility Services
NUSMWCHDE	National Union of Sheet Metal Workers, Coppersmiths, Heating and Domestic Engineers
NUT	National Union of Teachers
NUWDAT	National Union of Wallcoverings Decorative and Allied Trades
NV	naamloze vennootschap (Du: public limited liability company)
nw	narrow widths
NW	London North Western (postcode area)
NW	Northumbrian Water (RWA) (now NWG)
NW	north-west
NWC	National Wood Council (now amalgamated with TRADA)
NWC	North West Consortium
NWE	normal weekly earnings (re SMP)

NWG	Northumbrian Water Group		NWWA	North West Water Authority (RWA) (now NWWG)
NWHC	North Wessex Housing Consortium		NWWG	North West Water Group
NWLSA	North West London Society of Architects (RIBA branch)			
NWML	National Weights and Measures Laboratory (DTI)		NYK	North Yorkshire (BS county code)
NWP	numerical weather prediction (by computer)		NYM	Newry and Mourne, Northern Ireland (BS code)
NWR	National Working Rules		NYSE	New York Stock Exchange
NWSA	North Wales Society of Architects (SAW branch)		NYTG(HE)	North Yorkshire Technical Group (Housing and Environment)
NWTA	National Waterways Transport Association		NZIA	New Zealand Institute of Architects
NWTRHA	North West Thames Regional Health Authority		NZLR	*New Zealand Law Reports*

O

O	origin (graphs)		OCT	Overseas Countries and Territories of Member States (EC)
O	oxygen (chemical element)			
			OD	Ordnance Datum
OA	office automation		O/D	outside diameter
o/a	overall		ODA	office document architecture (computers)
OAC	Overseas Affairs Committee (RIBA)			
OAF	Ove Arup Foundation		ODA	Overseas Development Administration
OAL	Office of Arts and Libraries		ODI	Overseas Development Institute
O&M	organisation and method		ODL	Ordnance Datum Liverpool
OAP	old age pension/pensioner		ODM	Overseas Development Ministry
OAPEC	Organisation of Arab Petroleum Exporting Countries		ODN	Ordnance Datum Newlyn
			ODP	open distributed processing (computers)
OAS	on active service			
OAS	Organisation of American States		ODPR	Office of the Data Protection Registrar
OAU	Organisation of African Unity			
			OECD	Organisation for Economic Co-operation and Development (originally European as OEEC, now world-wide)
ob	*obiit* (Lat: he/she died; followed by date of death)			
OBE	Officer of the British Empire			
obit	obituary (notice of death)		OECE	Organisation Européenne de Coopération Économique (= EOEC)
OBN	overseas building note (BRE)			
o/c	overcharge		OECS	Organisation of East Caribbean States
ocn	open copper nailing			
OCPCA	Oil and Chemical Plant Construction Association		OED	*Oxford English Dictionary*
			OEDIPUS	Oxford English Dictionary integrating, proofing and updating system
OCR	optical character recognition			
oct	octave			
Oct	October			

81

OEEC	Organisation for European Economic Co-operation (now OECD)
OEM	original equipment manufacturer
OER	Office of Electricity Regulation
OETB	Offshore Energy Technology Board
Ofgas	Office of Gas Supply
OFID	OPEC Fund for International Development
OFT	Office of Fair Trading
OFTEL	Office of Telecommunications
OG	open ground or bare root (plants)
OG	ordinary glazing
OGM	ordinary general meeting
OGS	see Ofgas
OHB	Orkney Health Board
OHMS	On His/Her Majesty's Service
OIC	Organisation of the Islamic Conference
OIML	Organisation Internationale pour la Métrologie Légale (=IOLM)
OIS	office information system (computers)
OJ, OJEC	*Official Journal of the European Communities*
OK	orl korrect (all correct)
okta	one eighth of the sky
OL	not frost resistant and with low soluble salt content (bricks)
OL	Oldham (postcode area)
O-level	ordinary level (GCE)
OLP	Open Learning Project (RIBA)
OM	Order of Merit
OME	Office of Manpower Economics
OMH	Omagh, Northern Ireland (BS code)
OMR	optical mark reading (computers)
OMS	Organisation and Methods Society
OMV	open market value
ON	not frost resistant and with normal soluble salt content (bricks)
ONC	Ordinary National Certificate
OND	Ordinary National Diploma
ono	or near offer

ONP	open network provision (computers)
OP	occasional paper
OP	old person
op	*opus* (Lat: work)
OP	out of print
OPAC	on-line public access catalogue
OPAMP	operational amplifier
OPAS	Occupational Pensions Advisory Service
OPB	Occupational Pensions Board
OPC	ordinary Portland cement
op cit	*opere citato* (Lat: in the work quoted)
OP-CODE	operational code
OPCS	Office of Population Censuses and Surveys
OPD	old person's dwelling
OPD	out-patients department
OPEC	Organisation of Petroleum Exporting Countries
OPG	Overseas Projects Group
OPH	old people's home
OPM	optically projected map
opp	opposite
OQ	ordinary quality (bricks – pre-1985 designation)
OR	Official Receiver
OR	Official Referee
or	operational research
OR	a logic gate (computers)
ORACLE	optional reception of announcements by coded line electronics (ITV television newspaper)
ORGALIME	Organisation for liaison between European electrical and mechanical engineering industries
ORHA	Oxford Regional Health Authority
ORK	Orkney, Scotland (BS county code)
ORS	Operational Research Society
ortho	orthographic projection
OS	oil separator
OS	Ordnance Survey
OS	organic solvent (timber preservative)
Os	osmium (chemical element)
os	oversite (concrete layer)
OS/2	an IBM operating system (computers)

OSA	Oldham Society of Architects (part of RIBA Manchester branch)		OSS	Open Spaces Society (formerly CPS)
OSB	oriented stranded board		OT	Office of Telecommunications
OSBM	Ordnance Survey bench mark		OT	open top
OSF	Open Software Foundation		OT	overtime
OSI	open systems interconnection (ISO – computers)		OUP	Oxford University Press
oso	one side only			
OSRD	Office of Scientific Research and Development		OWS	Office of Water Services
OSRP	offices, shops and railway premises		OX	Oxford (postcode area)
OSRPA	Offices, Shops and Railway Premises Act		OXF	Oxfordshire (BS county code)
OSRV	Ordnance Survey Review Committee		oz	ounce
			ozt	ounce troy

P

P	Building fabric sundries (Common Arrangement)		P50	tax form: after four weeks unemployment
p	momentum		P60	statement of tax deducted – at end of year
p	page			
P	parity		P70(T)	notice of assessment (income tax)
P	parking, car park			
p	penny, pence		PA	nylon, polyamide
P	person		PA	Paintmakers Association of Great Britain
P	peta (multiple prefix: 10^{15})			
P	phon (unit of loudness)		PA	Paisley, Renfrewshire (postcode area)
P	phosphorus (chemical element)			
p	pico (submultiple prefix: 10^{-12})		Pa	pascal (unit of pressure or stress)
P	poise (CGS unit of dynamic viscosity)		PA	Pedestrians Association
			pa	*per annum* (Lat: for each year)
P	power (work done per second, measured in watts)		PA	personal architect (ECL program – computers)
P	President		PA	personal assistant
p	pressure (measured in Pa)		Pa	protactinium (chemical element)
P	private		PA	public address
			PABX	private automatic branch exchange
P1	tax return – lower-paid			
P2(T)	notice of coding (income tax)		PACD	UN Plan of Action to Combat Desertification
P11D	return (by employer) of expenses and allowances		PADT	Public Art Development Trust
P15	coding claim (income tax)		PAFL	Planning Aid for Londoners (RTPI) (now PAL)
P38(S)	tax form: student employed during college etc holiday		PAG	Plastics Art Group (EC: CCC)
P40	tax claim form		PAGB	Paintmakers Association of Great Britain
P45	statement of tax deducted – on leaving job		PAI	personal accident and illness (insurance)
P46	tax form: on starting new job			

PAID	Professional Assistance Indemnity Development scheme (RIBA)	PBR	pyridine-butadiene rubber
PAL	permanent artificial lighting	P/BS	persons per bedspace
PAL	phase alternation line (a colour TV system)	PBT	as PBTP
		PBTP	polybutylene terephthalate
PAL	Planning Aid for London (merger of LPAS and PAFL)	PBX	private branch exchange
PALO	police architectural liaison officer	pc	per cent (qv)
PAN	practice advice note (RTPI)	PC	personal computer
P&CR	Planning and Compensation Reports (law reports)	p/c	petty cash
		PC	polycarbonate
P&I	principal and interest	PC	Population Commission (UN: ECOSOC)
P&L	profit and loss	PC	Portland cement
p&p	postage and packing	PC	practical completion
p&s	planking and strutting	PC	prime cost
p&scr	plugged and screwed	PC	Privy Council, Privy Councillor
PAPC	Poster Advertising Planning Committee	PCA	Prestressed Concrete Association
PAR	parabolic aluminised reflector (electric light bulbs: PAR 38 and PAR 56)	PCB	polychlorinated biphenyl (toxic chemical)
		PCB	printed circuit board
PAR	programme analysis and review (DES)	PCC	Professional Conduct Committee (RIBA)
para	paragraph	PCCA	Precast Concrete Cladding Association
Parl	Parliament, parliamentary	PC-DOS	a disk operating system (MS-DOS adapted for IBM computers)
PARS	Pedestrians Association for Road Safety	pce	piece
PAS	public address system	PCFA	Precast Concrete Frame Association
PASC	Pacific Area Standards Congress	PCFC	Polytechnics and Colleges Funding Council
PASCAL	a high level computer programming language (after Blaise Pascal)	PCL	Polytechnic of Central London
PASG	Percent for Art Steering Group	PCN	personal communications network
PASRUK	Preliminary Assessment of Seismic Risk in the United Kingdom (research project)	PCP	pentachlorophenol (toxic dry rot treatment and preservative)
PAX	private automatic exchange	PCPL	pentachlorophenyllaurate (industrial preservative)
PAYE	pay as you earn	PC sum	prime cost sum
PB	performance bond	PCTFE	polychlorotrifluoroethylene (rubber – same as CFM)
PB	personal best	PCW	personal computer and word processor
PB	planning bulletin		
pb	plasterboard	Pd	paid
Pb	plumbum (lead – chemical element)	Pd	palladium (chemical element)
PB	polished brass	pd	per day
PB	polybutene 1	pd	per diem (Lat: for each day)
pbd	plasterboard	P/D	persons per dwelling
PBM	pivot bench mark (OS)	PD	Practice Data (RIBAS)
PBMA	Plastic Bath Manufacturers Association	PD	Product Data (RIBAS)
PBMA	Prefelted Board Manufacturers Association	PD	published document (BSI)
		PDAP	polydiallyl phthalate
PBMAGB	Prefabricated Building Manufacturers Association of Great Britain	PDCB	paradichlorobenzene
		PDN	public data network (computers)
		PDP	personal development plan
PBR	payment by results	PDQ	process data quickly

PDS	Philips Data Systems
PDV	permitted development value
PE	Peterborough (postcode area)
PE	Planning Exchange
PE	polyethylene, 'Polythene'
P/E	price/earning ratio
ped	pedestal
PEL	Polytechnic of East London (formerly NELP)
PEP	personal equity plan
PER	Professional Executive Register
per cent	*per centum* (Lat: for each hundred)
PERINORM	on-line database: European bibliographic standards information produced by BSI, AFNOR and DIN
perk	perquisite
perp	perpendicular
Perp	Perpendicular style
per pro	*per procurationem* (Lat: for and on behalf of)
persp	perspective
PERT	programme evaluation and review technique (computers)
PET	as PETP
PET	Personal Electronic Transactor (CBM microcomputer)
PET	potentially exempt transfer
Pete	Protective Equipment Test Effigy
PETP	polyester, polyethylene terephthalate
PETRA	Project of Equipment for Treatment of Radioactive Waste (ADECO)
PF	phenolic, phenol-formaldehyde
PF	pitch fibre
PFA	Power Fastenings Association
PFA	pulverised fuel ash
PFF	Precast Flooring Federation
PFMA	Phenolic Foam Manufacturers Association
PFR	prototype fast reactor
PG	pot grown or container grown (trees)
PG	PowerGen (= PGC)
PGC	Patent Glazing Conference
PGC	Power Generation Company (PowerGen)
PGCA	Patent Glazing Contractors Association
PG:CCC	Pilkington Glass: Customer Communications Centre
PGM	personal ground modeller (ECL program – computers)

pH	hydrogen ion concentration (measure of acidity)
P/H	persons per hectare
PH	Perth (postcode area)
PH	public health
PH	public house
PHAB	physically-handicapped and able-bodied
PHANG	Federation of Heathrow Anti-Noise Groups
PHAS	Public Health Advisory Service
PhD	Doctor of Philosophy
PHI	permanent health insurance
PHI	public health inspector
P/HR	persons per habitable room
PI	Phoenix Initiative (organisation to promote inner city regeneration)
PI	professional indemnity
PIA	Partitioning Industry Association
PIARC	Permanent International Association of Road Congresses
PIB	Prices and Incomes Board
PIC	property investment certificate
PICA	PSA Information on Construction and Architecture
PICC	Professional Institutions Council for Conservation
PICK	a multi-user operating system (computers)
PIF	practice index form (RIBA: CAS)
PIG	Pipeline Industries Guild
PIG	Project Information Group (DOE)
PILOT	a programming language for creating CAL packages (computers)
PIMS	purchase and improvement mortgage scheme
PIN	personal identification number
PINC	property income certificate
PIO	programmable input and output (computers)
PIP	peripheral interchange program (computers)
PISC	Programme for Inspection of Steel Components (JRC – reactor safety)
PITCOM	Parliamentary Information Technology Committee
PIW	period of incapacity for work
PIXEL	picture element (one of the dots which make up a screen image)
PJA	Pipe Jacking Association
Pl	Place

pl	plural
PL	Plymouth (postcode area)
P/L	profit and loss
PL/1	programming language 1 (a high level computer programming language)
PLA	Port of London Authority
PLACO	ISO Planning Committee
PLAN	programming language nineteen hundred series (ICL)
PLANEX	on-line database: community planning and related subjects (PE)
plas	plastics, plastic
PLATO	a CBL system (computers)
PLB	*Property Law Bulletin*
PLC	public limited company
PLD	Product Liability Directive (EC)
PLDMA	Plastics Land Drainage Manufacturers Association
PLI	public local inquiry
PL/M	programming language for microprocessors
PLO	Palestine Liberation Organisation
PLOPS	percentage level of performance scheme
PLR	*Estates Gazette Planning Law Reports*
PLSEC	Public and Local Service Efficiency Campaign
plstr	plaster
plur	plural
PLUS	Private List Updating Service (BSI)
PLUTO	pipe line under the ocean
PM	Parker Morris (housing standards)
pm	per month
pm	*post meridiem* (Lat: after midday)
PM	*post mortem* (Lat: after death)
PM	Prime Minister
Pm	promethium (chemical element)
pm	purpose-made
PMA	positive mental attitude
PMB	private mail bag
pmh	production per man hour
PMI	Project Management International
PML	Plymouth Marine Laboratory
PMMA	polymethyl, methacrylate polymer
PMP	poly 4-methyl pentene-1, methyl pentene
PMS	Project Management Shop (computers)
PMT	photo-mechanical transfer
PMTS	predetermined motion time system (work study)

PN	practice note
PNdB	perceived noise level
pnl	panel
PNL	Polytechnic of North London
pntg	pointing
po	planted on
Po	polonium (chemical element)
PO	Portsmouth (postcode area)
PO	Post Office
PO	prime only
POB	Post Office box
PoCo	Procedures for Political Co-operation (EC)
POEU	Post Office Engineering Union
POIPCD	Patent Office and Industrial Property and Copyright Department (DTI)
POM	acetal, polyoxymethylene, polyformaldehyde (a polyacetal)
pop	population
POP	Post Office preferred (envelope sizes)
POPA	Property Owners Protection Association
Por	Portugese
POR	Professional and Office Recruitment
POTS	plain old telephone system
POUCNI	Post Office Users Council for Northern Ireland
POUCS	Post Office Users Council for Scotland
POUCW	Post Office Users Council for Wales
POUNC	Post Office Users National Council
POW	Powys (BS county code)
POW	Prince of Wales
PP	education publications (BSI)
pp	pages
PP	Past President
pp	per pro (qv)
PP	polypropylene, copolymer in which propylene is the main constituent
PPE	personal protection equipment (EC term)
PPC	Professional Purposes Committee (ARCUK)
PPG	planning policy guidance note (DOE)
ppm	pages per minute
ppm	parts per million
PPMS	Plastic Pipe Manufacturers Society
PPO	as PPOX

PPOX	polyphenylene oxide
PPP	personal pension plan
PPRIBA	Past President of the RIBA
PPS	Parliamentary Private Secretary
PPS	*post post scriptum* (an additional PS (qv))
ppt	parapet
pr	pair
PR	plot ratio
Pr	praseodymium (chemical element)
PR	Preston (postcode Area)
PR	public relations
PRA	Paint Research Association
PRC	polyester resin concrete
prc	precast reinforced concrete
PRCA	Public Relations Consultants Association
prefab	prefabricated, a prefabricated building
prelim	preliminary
prelims	preliminaries – first section of bill of quantities
prep	preparatory (school)
prep	prepare, prepared, preparation
Pres	President
PRI	Plastics and Rubber Institute
PRIBA	President of the RIBA
Prin	Principal
PRO	Public Record Office
PRO	public relations officer
PROD	public request to order disposal (DOE scheme)
prof	professional
Prof	Professor
proj	projection
PROM	programmable read only memory (computers)
prop	proprietor
pro tem	*pro tempore* (Lat: for the time being)
prov	provisional
prov sum	provisional sum
prox	*proximo* (Lat: of next month)
PRP	profit-related pay
PRU	Pay Research Unit
PS	Parliamentary Secretary
PS	polystyrene, toughened polystyrene, modified polystyrene, styrene
PS	*post scriptum* (Lat: after what has been written – a note added at the end of a letter)
ps	pressed steel
PS	*Product Selector* (RIBAS)

PS	provisional sum
PS/2	an IBM range of personal computers
PSA	Property Services Agency (DOE)
PSALI	permanent supplementary artificial lighting of interiors
PSB	Polytechnic of the South Bank
PSBR	public sector borrowing requirement
PSBR	pyridine-styrene-butadiene rubber
PSD	personal site designer (ECL program – computers)
PSD	Public Supplies Directive (EC)
Pseud	pseudonym
psi	pounds per square inch
PSMA	Professional Services Management Association
PSS	packet switched service, packet switch stream (BT – electronic mail)
PSTN	public switched telephone network
PSum	provisional sum
P-System	an operating system (computers)
pt	part
PT	perseroan tarbates (limited company)
PT	Pilgrim Trust (grants for preservation etc)
pt	pint
Pt	platinum (chemical element)
PTAC	Pilkington Technical Advisory Centre
PTCG	Public Transport Campaign Group
PTCMA	Plastic Tank and Cistern Manufacturers Association
PTE	Passenger Transport Executive
PTFCE	polytrifluorochloroethylene
PTFE	polytetrafluoroethylene, 'Teflon'
PTM	pre-tender meeting
ptn	partition
PTO	please turn over
P-trap	trap to WC pan with horizontal final outlet
PTRC	Planning and Transport Research and Computation International Company
PTRC ERS	PTRC Education and Research Services
PTT	postal, telegraph and telephone authority (Europe and elsewhere)
PTV	passenger transport vehicle
Pty, pty	proprietary (of a company)
Pu	plutonium (chemical element)

PU	as PUR		pw	per week
PU	public utilities		PWA	Plastics Window Association
pub	public house		PWAQ	private with approximate quantities (version of SFBC)
PUG	Pafec User Group (computers)			
PULSE	Public and Local Service Efficiency Campaign		PWC	Portsmouth Water Company
			PWD	public works department
PUR	urethane, polyurethane, rigid polyurethane		PWD	Public Works Directive (EC)
			PWG	Plastics Windows Group (BPF)
PUT	property unit trust		PWI	Permanant Way Institution
			PWLB	Public Works Loan Board
PV	present value		PWMSCEC	Public Works and Municipal Services Congress and Exhibition Council
PVA	as PVAC or PVAL			
PVAC	polyvinyl acetate			
PVAL	polyvinyl alcohol		PWOQ	private without quantities (version of SFBC)
PVC	permanent virtual circuit (telecommunications)		PWQ	private with quantities (version of SFBC)
PVC	vinyl, polyvinyl chloride, copolymer in which vinyl chloride is the main constituent		PWR	pressurised water reactor
PVDC	polyvinylidene chloride			
PVDF	polyvinylidene fluoride		PX	private exchange
PVF	polyvinyl fluoride		PXQ	private without quantities (version of SFBC)
PVS	Pascal validation suite (computers)			

Q

Q	electrical charge		Q factor	a factor which describes the quality or selectivity of a circuit
Q	Paving/Planting/Fencing/Site furniture (Common Arrangement)			
Q	question		Qly	quarterly
			qm	*quantum meruit* (Lat: how much he has deserved)
QA	quality assurance			
Q&A	question and answer		QMS	quality management system
QAS	quality assessment schedule			
QAS	Quality Assurance Services (BSI or TRADA)		qr	quarter
QB	*Queen's Bench* (law reports)		QS	quality system
QBD	Queen's Bench Division (of High Court)		QS	quantity surveyor
			QSIN	quantity surveyor's information note (PSA)
QC	quality circles (management technique)		QSRMC	Quality Scheme for Ready Mixed Concrete
QC	quality control		QSS	quality system supplement
QC	Queen's Counsel			
			qt	quarry tile
QE2	Queen Elizabeth II		qt	quart
QED	*quod erat demonstrandum* (Lat: which was to be proved)		qt	quiet (also 'on the q.t.')
			qty	quantity

quad	quadrangle		qv	*quod vide* (Lat: which see)
QUADRO2	queues and delays at roadworks (DoT computer model)		Q-value	measure of energy released or absorbed in a nuclear reaction
QUALGO	quasi-autonomous local government organisation			
QUANGO	quasi-autonomous non-governmental organisation		QWERTY	the normal typewriter keyboard (the first six letters)
Q unit	unit used to express the world's fuel reserves		qy	query

R

R	Disposal systems (Common Arrangement)		RAIC	Royal Architectural Institute of Canada
R, r	radius		Ralta	Recreation and Leisure Trades Association
R	refrigerator			
R	*Regina* (Lat: Queen)		RAM	random access memory (computers)
R	resistance			
r	resistivity (thermal)		R&D	research and development
R	*Rex* (Lat: King)		R&D&D	research and development and demonstration
R	river			
r	roentgen (unit of radiation exposure)		R&IT	*Rating and Income Tax* (law reports)
R	see R-value		R&R	rest and recuperation
R	sound reduction index		RAP	research action programme
			RAPE	Richmond (upon Thames) Association for the Preservation of the Environment
Ra	radium (chemical element)			
RA	Ramblers Association			
RA	*Rating Appeals* (law reports)		RAPRA	Rubber and Plastics Research Association
RA	regional architect (NHS)			
RA	Royal Academician		RARDE	Royal Armament Research and Development Establishment (Christchurch)
RA	Royal Academy of Arts			
RAADP	Royal Association in Aid of Deaf People			
RABRM	Research Associations of British Rubber Manufacturers		RB	river board
			RB	root balled (plants)
RACE	Research and Development in Advanced Communications Technology in Europe (EC)		Rb	rubidium (chemical element)
			RBA	Refined Bitumen Association
			RBIT	see RIBABIT
rad	radian (unit of plane angle)		RBM	rivet bench mark (OS)
rad	radiator		RBN	Register of Business Names
rad	radius			
rad	rad (unit of absorbed radiation)		RC	reinforced concrete
radar	radio detection and ranging		RC	resistance-capacitance
RADAR	Royal Association for Disability and Rehabilitation		RC	Roman Catholic
			RCA	reduced covered area
RADD	Royal Association in Aid of the Deaf and Dumb		RCA	Royal College of Art
			RCAHMW	Royal Commission on Ancient and Historical Monuments in Wales
RAI	Royal Archaeological Institute			
RAIA	Royal Australian Institute of Architects		R$_{CAV}$	thermal resistence of cavity

RCC	Railway Conversion Campaign	ret	retired
rccb	residual current circuit breaker	rev	revision, revised
rcd	residual current device	rev	revolution
RCEP	Royal Commission on Environmental Pollution	RF	radio frequency
RCHME	Royal Commission on the Historic Monuments of England	RFAC	registered firm of assessed capability
RCR	*Rules for Compositors and Readers*	RFAC	Royal Fine Art Commission
		rf&r	return, fill and ram
R/D	refer to drawer	rf&s	render, float and set
Rd	Road	RFH	Royal Festival Hall
RDA	remote database access (computers)	RFS	registered firms scheme of assessed capability (BSI)
RDA	Royal Docks Association	RFS	Registry of Friendly Societies
RDA	rural development area	RFS	Royal Forestry Society of England, Wales and Northern Ireland
RDC	Rural Development Commission (= merger of CoSIRA and Development Commission)		
		RG	Reading (postcode area)
RDC	rural district council (pre-1974)	RGB	red, green, blue
RDI	Distinction of Royal Design for Industry	RGS	Royal Geographical Society
RDOS	a disk operating system (computers)	RH	Redhill (postcode area)
		RH	relative humidity
RDV	realised development value	Rh	rhodium (chemical element)
		RHA	regional health authority
RE	regional engineer (NHS)	RHA	Road Haulage Association
Re	rhenium (chemical element)	RHA	Royal Hibernian Academy
RE	rodding eye	rh&s	rivet head and snap
reb	rebated	RHASS	Royal Highland and Agricultural Society of Scotland
rebar	reinforcement bar		
recd	received	RHB	regional hospitals board (NHS)
red	reduce, reduced	RHPC	rapid-hardening Portland cement
Reg	region, regional	RHS	rectangular hollow section
reg	registered	RHS	right-hand side
RegArch	Registered Architect	RHS	rolled hollow section
Regs	regulations	RHS	Royal Horticultural Society
REHAB	Rehabilitation of the Disabled		
REHIS	Royal Environmental Health Institute of Scotland	RIAI	Royal Institute of the Architects of Ireland
reinf	reinforced, reinforcement	RIAS	Royal Incorporation of Architects in Scotland
rem	remove		
rem	roentgen equivalent man/ mammal (dose of radiation related to biological effect)	RIBA	Member of the RIBA
		RIBA	Royal Institute of British Architects
REMCO	ISO committee on reference materials	RIBABIT	RIBA Building Industry Trust (formerly RIBACF)
Ren	Renaissance	RIBACAD	RIBA CAD (RIBAS product drawings service for use with CAD)
RENAVAL	EC programme supporting regeneration of former shipbuilding and shiprepairing areas		
		RIBACF	RIBA Conference Fund (now RIBABIT)
rep	roentgen equivalent physical (radiation)	RIBAIA	RIBA Insurance Agency
		RIBAIR	RIBA Indemnity Research
REPB	regional economic planning board	RIBAP	RIBA Publications
		RIBAS	RIBA Services
REPC	regional economic planning council	RICS	Royal Institution of Chartered Surveyors

RICSIS	RICS Insurance Services
RIGB	Royal Institution of Great Britain
RIP	rather important person
RIP	*requiescat/requiescant in pace* (Lat: may he/she/they rest in peace)
RIPA	Royal Institute of Public Administration
RIPE	Radical Improvements for Peripheral Estates
RIPHH	Royal Institute of Public Health and Hygiene
RISC	reduced instruction set computer
RJE	remote job entry (computers)
rkg	raking
rl	rail
RL	reduced level
RLTA	see Ralta
RM	Romford (postcode area)
rm	room
RMAGB	Recreation Managers Association of Great Britain
RMC	ready-mixed concrete
RMMCA	Road Marking Manufacturers and Contractors Association
RMS	root mean square
RMSO	regional management services officer (NHS)
Rn	radon (chemical element)
RNIB	Royal National Institute for the Blind
RNID	Royal National Institute for the Deaf
RO	record office
ro	rough
ro	round
ROA	return on assets
Roc	rococo style
ROI	return on investment
roj	rake out joints
ROM	read only memory (computers)
Rom	Romanesque style
rom	roman (type)
ROSCO	Road Operators Safety Council
RoSPA	Royal Society for the Prevention of Accidents
RP	registered plumber
RP	reinforced plastics
RP	report program generator (a business programming language – computers)

RPA	Rubber and Plastics Association
RPB	recognised professional body
RPB	river purification board
rph	revolutions per hour
RPI	retail price index
RPM	retail price maintenance
rpm	revolutions per minute
RPRAGB	see RAPRA
rps	revolutions per second
RPS	Rural Planning Services
RQS	regional quantity surveyor
RR	Refurbishment Register
RR	research reactor
RRC	*Ryde's Rating Cases* (law reports)
RRP	recommended retail price
RS	Royal Society
R_s	surface resistance to heat flow
RS232	a standard serial interface for personal computers
RSA	Rating Surveyors Association
RSA	Regional Studies Association
RSA	response selection amplifier
RSA	Royal Scottish Academy
RSA	Royal Society of Arts (Royal Society for the Encouragement of Arts, Manufactures and Commerce)
RSAS	Royal Sanitary Association of Scotland
RSC	random security check
RSDA	Road Surface Dressing Association
RSE	Royal Society of Edinburgh
RSFS	Royal Scottish Forestry Society
RSG	rate support grant
RSG	regional seats of government (bomb-proof complexes)
RSGM	Register of Safety Glazing Marks
RSGS	Royal Scottish Geographical Society
RSH	Royal Society (for the Promotion) of Health
RSI	repetitive stress injury
R_{si}	surface resistance to heat flow – internal surface
RSJ	rolled steel joist
RSNC	Royal Society for Nature Conservation
R_{so}	surface resistence to heat flow – outside surface
RSPA	Royal Society for the Prevention of Accidents (RoSPA)
RSPB	Royal Society for the Protection of Birds

91

RS series	recommendations on data transmission (IEEE)	RUG	Robocom User Group (computers)
RSUA	Royal Society of Ulster Architects	RUG	Rucaps User Group (computers)
RSVP	*répondez s'il vous plait* (Fr: please reply)	Russ	Russian
		RV	ratable value
RT	reverberation time	RVA	Rating and Valuation Association
RTA	Roofing Tile Association	R-value	thermal resistance of construction (reciprocal of U-value)
RTC	regional technology centre (DES)		
RTD	research and technological development	r-value	thermal resistivity of material (reciprocal of k-value)
Rt Hon	Right Honourable	RVR	*Rating and Valuation Recorder* (law reports)
RTL	resistor transistor logic		
RTPI	Royal Town Planning Institute		
RTT	Rose Theatre Trust	RWA	Member of the Royal West of England Academy
RTU	roof tile underlay		
RTZ	Rio Tinto-Zinc Corporation	RWA	regional water authority
		RWC	Rickmansworth Water Company
Ru	ruthenium (chemical element)	RWEA	Royal West of England Academy
RUCAPS	really useful computer-aided production system (originally Riyadh University . . .) (CAD system)	RWH	rainwater head
		RWMAC	Radioactive Waste Management Advisory Committee
RUDAT	regional and urban design assistance team (USA)	RWO	rainwater outlet
		RWP	rainwater pipe
RUF	rigid urethane foam	RWS	rainwater shoe

S

S	entropy	SA	Society of Archivists
S	Piped supply systems (Common Arrangement)	SA	soil applied (herbicide)
		SA	Soil Association
s	second (unit of time – SI basic unit)	SA	special area (DOE)
		SA	Swansea (postcode area)
s	section	SAA	silver anodised aluminium
S	Sheffield (postcode area)	SAA	Society of Architect Artists
s	shilling	SAA	Suffolk Association of Architects (RIBA branch)
S	shower unit		
S	siemens (unit of electric conductance)	SAA	system application architecture (computers)
S	sink	SAAT	Society of Architectural and Associated Technicians (now BIAT)
S	south		
S	standard hardboard		
S	sulfur (chemical element)	SABA	Scottish Aggregate Block Association
S1, S2, S3	structural softwood classification groups	SABE	School of Architecture and Building Engineering (University of Bath)
S100	a standard bus (computers)		
		SAC	Scottish Arts Council
SA	société anonyme, sociedad anónima (Fr, Sp: limited company)	SACTRA	Standing Advisory Committee on Trunk Road Assessment
		SADC	Scottish Agricultural Development Council

SADCC	South African Development Co-ordination Conference
SADG	Société des Architectes Diplômés par le Gouvernement (Society of Government Certified Architects – France)
SADWSS	Scottish Association of Directors of Water and Sewerage Services
SAE	Society of Automotive Engineers (USA)
sae	stamped addressed envelope
SAEM	Suspended Access Equipment Manufacturers
SAE numbers	
	arbitrary classification by the SAE of lubricating oil based on viscosity
SAG	Salaried Architects Group (RIBA)
SAGA	Sand and Gravel Association
SAHGB	Society of Architectural Historians of Great Britain
SAI	Society of Architectural Illustrators
SAID	School of Architecture and Interior Design (Brighton Polytechnic)
SAIL	Safety in Leisure Research Unit
SAM	a CBL system (computers)
SAN	styrene-acrilonitrile copolymer
S&L	sale and leasehold
s&l	spread and levelled
s&s	sides and soffits
s&s	spigots and sockets
s&vp	soil and vent pipe
san ftgs	sanitary fittings
SAR	soil applied residual (herbicide)
SARL	sociedade anônima de responsabilidade limitada (joint stock company of limited liability)
SARL	société á responsabilité limitée (limited company)
SAS	Search and Advisory Service of the UK Patent Office
Sat	Saturday
SAT	soil applied transient (herbicide)
SAUS	School for Advanced Urban Studies (University of Bristol)
sav	stock at valuation
SAVE	Save Britain's Heritage
SAW	Society of Architects in Wales
SAYE	save as you earn
Sb	stibium (antimony – chemical element)
SB	sub-basement
SBCA	Scottish Building Contractors Association

SBCC	Scottish Building Contract Committee
SBEF	Scottish Building Employers Federation
SBGI	Society of British Gas Industries
SBH	Save Britain's Heritage (SAVE)
SBI	*Sell's Building Index*
SBI	Statens Byggeforskningsinstitut (Danish Building Research Institute)
SBR	Scottish Building Regulations
SBR	single bedroom
SBR	Stiching Bouwresearch (Building Research Foundation – Netherlands)
SBR	styrene-butadiene rubber
SBS	sick building syndrome
SC	satin chrome
Sc	scandium (chemical element)
SC	School Certificate
Sc	science
SC	Security Council (UN)
sc	self-contained
SC	*Session Cases* (Scotland – law reports)
sc	small capitals
SC	Sports Council
SC	Statistical Commission (UN: ECOSOC)
SC	stop cock
Sc	stratocumulus (cloud classification)
SC	subcontract, subcontractor
SCA	Sectional Chambers Association
SCA	Sprayed Concrete Association
SCA	Suspended Ceilings Association
SCALA	Society of Chief Architects of Local Authorities
SCAR	Standing Committee on Agricultural Research (EC)
SCAUM	Standing Conference of Archaeological Unit Managers
SCBCO	Society of Chief Building Control Oficers
SCC	Scottish Consumer Council
SCC	Structural Concrete Consortium
SCCBAJA	Scottish County, City and Burgh Architects Joint Association
SCCBMG	Standing Consultative Committee on Building Materials Group (DOE)
SCCMENH	Steering Committee for the Conservation and Management of the Environment and Natural Habitat (Council of Europe)

SCDI	Scottish Council of Development and Industry
SCE	Scottish Certificate of Education
SCEALA	Standing Conference of East Anglian Local Authorities
SCET	Society of Civil Engineering Technicians
SCF	Scientific Committee for Food (EC)
SCFBAC	Scottish Central Fire Brigades Advisory Council
SCHOSA	Standing Conference of Heads of Schools of Architecture
SCI	Society of Chemical Industry
SCI	Steel Construction Institute (formerly CONSTRADO)
SCICHH	Steering Committee for Integrated Conservation of the Historic Heritage (Council of Europe)
SCIENCE	Stimulate the International Co-operation and Interchange needed by European Research Scientists (EC)
SCIL	Small Computers in Libraries (annual exhibition and conference; now just CIL)
sckt	socket
SCLFM	Society of Chain Link Fencing Manufacturers
SCMS	serial copy management system (to prevent copies of copies of CDs – computers)
SCMS	Standing Committee of Member States' Representatives (EC)
SCNI	Sports Council for Northern Ireland
SCOLA	Second Consortium of Local Authorities
Scot	Scotland, Scottish
SCOTEC	Scottish Technical Education Council
SCPS	Society of Civil and Public Servants
SCQSLG	Society of Chief Quantity Surveyors in Local Government
scr	screw
SCR	styrene-chloroprene rubber
SCRATA	Steel Castings Research and Trade Association
SCRMM	Steering Committee on Regional and Municipal Matters
SCS	sectional completion supplement (to standard form of contract)
SCS	Society of Company Secretaries
SCSS	Standing Committee on Structural Safety

SCW	Sports Council for Wales
sd	screw down (valve)
s/d	semi-detached
sd	*sine die* (Lat: with no appointed date)
SD	site direction
SDA	Scottish Development Agency
SDA	Sex Discrimination Act
SDC	Scottish Design Centre
SDC	Sheffield Development Corporation
SDD	Scottish Development Department
SDG	Spitalfields Development Group
SDI	selective dissemination of information
Sdn Bhd	sendirian berhad (private limited company)
SDO	special development order
SDR	special drawing rights (IMF)
SDWC	Sutton District Water Company
SDW.T	see SON
SE	London South Eastern (postcode area)
Se	selenium (chemical element)
SE	Society of Engineers
SE	south-east
SE	Southern Electric
SE	Stock Exchange
SEA	Single European Act
SEATO	South East Asia Treaty Organisation
SEBCC	South East Building Control Consortium
sec	secant
Sec	Secretary
sec	section
SECED	Society for Earthquake and Civil Engineering Dynamics
sect	section
SED	Scottish Education Department
SEDOC	Système Européen de Diffusion des Offres et des demandes d'emploi enregistrées en compensation internationale (EC job vacancy information scheme)
SE-duct	South Eastern duct
SEE	Society of Environmental Engineers
SEEBOARD	South Eastern Electricity Board
SEGAS	South Eastern Gas Board
SELTEC	South East London Technical College
SEM	Single European Market
SEM	Southern and Eastern Mediterranean Countries

SEMA	Storage Equipment Manufacturers Association	SGM	South Glamorgan (BS county code)
Semlac	South East Midlands Local Authority Consortium	SGM	special general meeting
Sep, Sept	September	SGMGA	Scottish Glass Merchants and Glaziers Association
SERA	self-employed retirement annuity	SGML	standard generalised markup language (computers)
SERA	Socialist Environment and Resources Association	SGNBT	Subdirección General Normativa Básica y Tecnologica/MOPU
SERC	Science and Engineering Research Council		(National Institute for Quality in Building – Spain)
SERPLAN	London and South East Regional Planning Conference	SGNPLABC	Steering Group for the National Promotion of Local Authority
SERPS	State Earnings-Related Pension Scheme		Building Control
SERRL	South East Regional Research Laboratory (Birkbeck College, London)	SGS	Scottish Geographic Society
		SGT	Society of Gas Technology
SET	selective employment tax (1966-72)	SH	Scottish Homes (merger of SSHA and HCAS)
SETRHA	South East Thames Regional Health Authority	S/H	shorthand
		SH	side-hung
SF	sinking fund	SH	specific heat
SF	standard form (of building contract)	SHA	Scottish Heritage Agency
		SHA	Southwark Heritage Association
SF	Stone Federation	SHAC	Shelter Housing Aid Centre
S/F	supply and fix	SHARE	Shelter Housing Aid Renewal Experiment
SFAC	Solid Fuel Advisory Council		
SFAS	Solid Fuel Advisory Service	SHB	Shetland Health Board
SfB	Samarbetskommittén för Byggnadsfrågor (Co-ordinating Committee for the Building Industry – the Swedish committee that devised the SfB classification system) (see also CI/SfB)	SHBF	Sussex Housing and Building Forum
		SHELTER	National Campaign for the Homeless
		SHF	super high frequency
		SHNC	Scottish Higher National Certificate
		SHND	Scottish Higher National Diploma
SFBC	Standard Form of Building Contract (usually refers to JCT 80)	SHR	Shropshire (BS county code)
		SHSA	South Humberside Society of Architects (RIBA branch)
SFBIU	Scottish Farm Buildings Investigation Unit	SHSSB	Southern Health and Social Services Board (Northern Ireland)
SFCA	Standard Form of Cost Analysis (RICS)	S/HT	shorthand typist
SFEEC	Social Fund of EEC	SI	Shirley Institute (textile research and testing)
SFK	Suffolk (BS county code)		
SFTC	Swedish Finnish Timber Council	Si	silicon (chemical element)
		Si	silicone rubber
SG	Secretary General	SI	silicone, substituted polysiloxane (plastic)
SG	special glazing		
SG	specific gravity	SI	Society of Indexers
SG	Stevenage, Hertfordshire (postcode area)	SI	statutory instrument (HMSO)
		SI	Système International d'Unités (SI units – the universal metric system)
SG	street gulley		
SGA	see SAGA		
SGB	Scaffolding Great Britain	SIA	Structural Insulation Association
SGHWR	steam generating heavy water reactor	SIAD	Society of Industrial Artists and Designers

SIC	special inductive capacity (electricity)		SLF	Scottish Landowners Federation
SIC	Standard Industrial Classification		SLI	see SOX
SIEH	Scottish Institute of Environmental Health		SLOAP	space left over after planning
			SLR	satellite laser ranging (OS)
SIESO	Society of Industrial Emergency Services Officers		SLRRACS	Society of Lloyd's Register Refrigeration and Air Conditioning Services
SIL	speech interference level (subjective loudness scale)		SLT	Scots Law Times (law reports)
SIM	Survey Information on Microfilm (OS)		Sm	samarium (chemical element)
			sm	smooth
SIMA	Steel Industry Management Association		SM	Sutton, Surrey (postcode area)
			SMATV	satellite master antenna television
sin	sine		SMBA	Scottish Marine Biological Association
sing	singular			
SIR	styrene-isoprene rubber		SME	small and medium-sized enterprises
SISCOT	Securities Industry Steering Committee on Taurus		SMIC	study of man's impact on climate
SITC	Standard International Trade Classification		SMIL/PDS	Statistics and Market Intelligence Library and Products Data Store (DTI)
SITM	Society of Information Technology Managers		SMM	Standard Method of Measurement of Building Works
SITPRO	Simplification of Trade Procedures		SMP	statutory maternity pay
			SMR	Greater London Sites and Monuments Record
sj	soldered joint			
SJ	Solicitor's Journal (law reports)		SMT	Soane Monuments Trust
SJIB	Scottish Joint Industry Board for the Electrical Contracting Industry		SMT	surface mount technology (computers)
			Sn	stannum (tin – chemical element)
SK	Stockport, Cheshire (postcode area)		SN	stop notice
			SN	Swindon (postcode area)
sktg	skirting		SNA	system network architecture (IBM version of OSI – computers)
sl	short length		SNARF	systematic numerical analysis of the risk of fire (computerised modelling technique)
SL	Slough (postcode area)			
SL	subject list (BSI)			
SLA	Security Locks Association		SNAS	Safe Neighbourhoods Advisory Service
SLA	Small Landlords Association			
SLA	Special Libraries Association		SNC	Scottish National Certificate
SLABS	School of Land and Building Studies		SND	Scottish National Diploma
			SNG	substitute natural gas
SLACE	see SOLACE		SNHTPC	Scottish National Housing and Town Planning Council
SLADE	Society of Lithographic Artists, Designers, Engravers and Process Workers		SNIPEF	Scottish and Northern Ireland Plumbing Employers Federation
SLAG	Save London Action Group		snk	sunk
SLASH	Scottish Local Authorities Special Housing Group (disbanded 1986)		SNR	signal-to-noise ratio (telecommunications)
SLC	South London Consortium (housing)		SO	Southampton (postcode area)
			so	spell out (printing)
SLCC	Society of Local Council Clerks		SO	standing order
SLCP	Society of Leisure Consultants and Publishers		SO	supervising officer
			Soc	society
SLCR	Scottish Land Court Reports (law reports)		SOD	Shorter Oxford Dictionary

SOED	*Shorter Oxford English Dictionary*
soff	soffit
SOGAT	Society of Graphical and Allied Trades
SOLACE	Society of Local Authority Chief Executives
SOLGCMEE	Society of Local Government Chief Mechanical and Electrical Engineers
Sols	solicitors
SOM	Somerset (BS county code)
SOM	start of message
SOMP	statement of objectives and management procedures (QA)
SON, SONDL, SON-L, SON-R, SON-TD, SDW.T	high pressure sodium discharge lamps
SONAR	sound navigation and ranging
SONET	synchronous optical network
SOS	international distress signal
SOS	Save our Saplings (Tree Council)
SOS	Save Our Services (transport)
SOS	silicon on sapphire (computers)
SOS	Stars Organisation for Spastics
SOX, SLI	low pressure sodium discharge lamps
SP	Salisbury (postcode area)
SP	Scottish Power
SP	single person
sp	small pipe
Sp	Spanish
SpA	società per azioni (It: joint stock company)
SPA	special protection area (for wild birds)
SPAB	Society for the Protection of Ancient Buildings
SPAID	Society for the Prevention of Asbestosis and Industrial Diseases
SPARTECA	South Pacific Regional Trade and Economic Co-operation Agreement (SPC)
SPATA	Swimming Pool and Allied Trades Association
SPC	South Pacific Commission
SPC	stored program control (computers)
spcg	spacing
SPD	single person's dwelling
SPEC	South Pacific Bureau for Economic Co-operation (SPC)
spec	specification
spec	speculative
spgr	specific gravity
SPISE	Sane Planning in the South-East
SPL	sound pressure level

SPLF	Society for the Protection of Life from Fire
splyd	splayed
SPMC	Southern Pine Marketing Council (USA)
SPNC	Society for the Promotion of Nature Conservation
SPNR	Society for the Promotion of Nature Reserves
SPOOL	simultaneous peripheral operation on-line (computers)
SPOT	single property owner trust
SPP	Standard of Professional Performance (RIBA)
SPRA	Single Ply Roofing Association
SPRINT	Strategic Programme for Innovation and Technology Transfer (EC)
SPRU	Science Policy Research Unit
SPSE	see SPISE
SPSE	Structure Plan for the South East
SPZ	simplified planning zone
SQ	special quality (bricks – pre-1985 designation)
Sq	Square
sq	square
sq ft	square foot/feet
sq in	square inch/inches
SQU	Standards and Quality Unit (DTI)
SQUID	superconducting quantum interference device
Sr	senior
sr	steradian (unit of solid angle)
Sr	strontium (chemical element)
SR	Sunderland (postcode area)
SRAMA	Spring Research and Manufacturers Association
SR and O	statutory rules and orders (now SI) (HMSO)
SRC	Science Research Council
SRC	Social Research Council
SRC	Strathclyde Regional Council
SRD	Safety and Reliability Directorate (UKAEA)
SRD	Sociological Research Division (HDD)
SRDB	Scientific Research and Development Branch (Home Office)
SrL	società a responsabilità limitata (limited liability company)
SRO	statutory rules and orders (now SI) (HMSO)
SRPB	Solway River Purification Board
SRPC	sulphate-resisting Portland cement

SRY	Surrey (BS county code)
SS	Secretary of State
SS	Southend-on-Sea (postcode area)
SS	Spastics Society
SS	special structural (structural softwood classification)
SS	stainless steel
SSA	Salop Society of Architects (RIBA branch)
SSA	Sheffield Society of Architects (RIBA branch)
SSA	Stirling Society of Architects (RIAS chapter)
SSAA	Scottish Society of Architect Artists
SSAC	Stainless Steel Advisory Centre
SSAP	statement of standard accounting practice
SSB	state sickness benefit
SSC	Scottish Sports Council
SSE	south-south-east
SSEB	South of Scotland Electricity Board
SSECC	South of Scotland Electricity Consultative Council
SSFF	Solid Smokeless Fuels Federation
SSG	extra-special glazing
SSHA	Scottish Special Housing Association (now merged with HCAS as Scottish Homes)
SSI	small scale integration (computers)
SSIC	Steel Sheet Information Centre
SSMA	Spiral Stair Manufacturers Association
SSP	statutory sick pay
SSPR	Standards for School Premises Regulations
SSRC	Social Science Research Council
SSSI	sites of special scientific interest
SSSWC	Sunderland and South Shields Water Company
SST	Scottish Sculpture Trust
SST	Society of Surveying Technicians
SST	supersonic transport
SSW	south-south-west
SSWC	South Staffordshire Water Company
St	saint
ST	Severn Trent (formerly STW)
St	Stanton number (used in forced convection studies)
ST	Stoke-on-Trent (postcode area)
St	stokes (CGS unit of kinematic viscosity)
ST	stop valve
st	store
St	stratus (cloud classification)
St	Street
STA	Solar Trade Association
STABEX	Stability in Export Revenue (ACP)
STACO	ISO Standing Committee for the Study of Principles of Standardisation
STAMP	Supervisory, Technical, Administrative, Managerial and Professional (UCATT white-collar section)
stats	photostats, photocopies
stats	statistics
STB	Scottish Tourist Board
STB	Strabane, Northern Ireland (BS code)
STC	Scientific and Technical Committee (EURATOM)
STC	Simon's Tax Cases (law reports)
STC	Swedish Timber Council
STCELA	Standing Technological Conference of European Local Authorities (IULA)
STD	Strathclyde Region, Scotland (BS code)
STD	subscriber trunk dialling
STEP	Standard for the Exchange of Product Model Data (ISO – computers)
STG	Scottish Transport Group
STMS	short term monetary support (EMS)
STOL	short take-off and landing
STOP	Stop Selling Our Past
STP	standard temperature and pressure
St P	stand pipe
STPG	Severn Tidal Power Group
STPT	Society of Town Planning Technicians
STRAD	signal transmitting receiving and distributing
S-trap	trap to WC pan with vertical final outlet
STRI	Sports Turf Research Institute
STRIVE	Society for the Preservation of Rural Industries and Village Enterprises
STS	Staffordshire (BS county code)
STUC	Scottish Trades Union Congress
STV	single transferable vote
STW	Severn-Trent Water (RWA) (now ST)
STW	sewage treatment works

STX	start of text
SU	slab urinal
SUAC	Steel Users Advisory Centre
sub	subcontractor
sub	subscription
subbie	subcontractor
SubC	subcontractor
Sun	Sunday
super	superficial, square, in area
Super	superintendent
supp, suppl	supplement, supplementary
Supt	superintendent
surf	surface
surr	surround
Surv	survey, surveyor
SUSI	Supply of Updated/Unpublished Survey Information (OS)
susp	suspended
SUT	Society for Underwater Technology
SV	safety valve
Sv	sievert (unit of dose equivalent – radiation)
SV	sluice valve
svp	*s'il vous plait* (Fr: if it pleases you, please)
SVP	soil vent pipe
SW	London South Western (postcode area)
SW	small works
SW	softwood

SW	Southern Water (formerly SWA)
SW	south-west
sw	stoneware
Sw	Swedish
SWA	Southern Water Authority (RWA) (now SW)
SWA	Steel Window Association
SWBCC	South-West Building Control Consortium
swd	softwood
SWE	South Wales Electricity
SWEB	South Western Electricity Board
SWG	standard wire guage
SWIE	South Wales Institute of Engineers
SWL	sound power level
SWOT	strengths weaknesses opportunities threats
SWS	surface water sewer
SWTRHA	South West Thames Regional Health Authority
SWW	South West Water (RWA)
SY	Shrewsbury (postcode area)
SYK	South Yorkshire (BS county code)
syll	syllabus
sym	symmetrical
syn	synonymous
SYSMIN	System for Safeguarding and Developing Mineral Production (ACP)
Systran	Co-ordination of national policies relating to machine or machine-assisted translation (EC)

T

T	Mechanical heating/cooling/refrigeration systems (Common Arrangement)
T	period (time occupied by one complete vibration or oscillation)
T	temperature
T	tera (multiple prefix: 10^{12})
T	tesla (unit of magnetic flux density)
T	time
T	ton
t	tonne
T	Treasury
T	trichromatic (see T unit)

T	Tuesday
t^2	the product of teamwork and technology (t^2 Solutions, formerly GMW Computers)
T2000	TRANSPORT 2000 (national environmental pressure group)
Ta	tantalum (chemical element)
TA	Taunton, Somerset (postcode area)
TA	Training Agency (formerly MSC and then TC)
tab	tablespoon

TAB	Technical Assistance Board (UN)
TAC	Taurus account controller
TAC	total allowable catch (fisheries)
TACS	total access communications system
TAG	Transbinary Architecture Group
TAI	International Atomic Time (standard against which UTC is compared)
tan	tangent
t&g	tongued and grooved
t&r	tread and riser
TAS	technical advisory service
TAS	Thatching Advisory Service
TASS	Technical Administrative and Supervisory Section (AUEW) (now merged with ASTMS as MSF)
Taunt	*Taunton Reports* (law reports)
TAURUS	transfer and automated registration of uncertified stock (Stock Exchange scheme) (see also SISCOT and TAC)
TAY	Tayside Region, Scotland (BS code)
Tb	terbium (chemical element)
TBBH	Traditional British Broadleaf Heritage
TBG	Tidy Britain Group
TBM	temporary bench mark
TBM	tunnel-boring machine
TBMA	Timber Buildings Manufacturers Association
TBTO	tributyltin oxide (timber preservative)
TC	*Tax Cases* (law reports)
Tc	technetium (chemical element)
TC	technical committee (EC)
TC	Technical Consultancy (BRE)
TC	terracotta
TC	Training Commission (see TA)
TC	Tree Council
TCB	Thames Conservancy Board
tcd	traced
TCDC	Technical Co-operation between Developing Countries
TCDG	Technical Co-ordination and Defence of Independent Groups (EC)
TCI	total cost indicator (Housing Corporation – from April 1989; see also TIC)
TCNMC	Transport Consortium of Non-Metropolitan Counties (Shires PTC)

TCP	town and country planning
TCPA	Town and Country Planning Association
TCS	The Crown Suppliers
TCU	transmission control unit (computers)
TD	Galashiels, Selkirkshire (postcode area)
TDA	Timber Development Association
TDC	Teesside Development Corporation
TDC	Telford Development Corporation
TDM	time-division multiplexing (telecommunications)
TDN	technical data notes
Te	tellurium (chemical element)
TE	tempered hardboard – extra density
TEA	tunnel emission amplifier
TEC	Technician Education Council
TEC	training and enterprise council
TED	Tenders Electronic Daily (EC on-line databank)
TEMA	Telecommunication Engineering and Manufacturing Association
temp	temperature
temp	temporary
TERN	training for evaluation and repair of non-traditional buildings
TESSA	tax exempt special savings account
TETOC	Technical Education and Training Organisation for Overseas Countries
TF	Telford, Salop (postcode area)
TFAP	Tropical Forestry Action Plan
TGO	Timber Growers Organisation
TGWU	Transport and General Workers Union
th	thick
Th	thorium (chemical element)
Th	Thursday
TH	top-hung
THB	Tayside Health Board
THE	Technical Help to Exporters (BSI service)
thrtd	throated
THS	The Hydrographic Society
Thurs	Thursday
THWC	Tendring Hundred Water Company
THWM	Trinity high water mark

TI	Technical Indexes
Ti	titanium (chemical element)
TIB	Technische Informationsbibliothek (Library for Technical Information – West Germany)
tic	take into consideration
TIC	total indicative cost (Housing Corporation – pre-April 1989; see also TCI)
TICA	Thermal Insulation Contractors Association
TIG	technical information group
TIHR	Tavistock Institute of Human Relations
TIMS	The Institute of Management Services
TIMSA	Thermal Insulation Manufacturers and Suppliers Association
tiros	television infra-red observation satellite
TIS	Tar Industries Services
TIS	Thematic Information Service (NERC)
TJV	Translink Joint Venture (channel tunnel construction consortium)
Tl	thallium (chemical element)
TLMA	Tunnel Lining Manufacturers Association
TLR	*Times Law Reports*
TLV	threshold limit value (permitted average concentration of constituents of air; see also CL)
TLV-C	TLV: concentration safety limit (see also CL)
TLV-STEL	TLV: short-term exposure limit
TLV-TWA	TLV: time-weighted average
Tm	thulium (chemical element)
TM	trade mark
TMA	Telecommunications Managers Association
TML	Transmanche Link (Anglo-French channel tunnel construction consortium)
TN	tempered hardboard – normal density
TN	Tonbridge, Kent (postcode area)
tngd	tongued
TNS	tender for nominated supplier
TNS/1	Nominated Supplier Tender for use with JCT 80

TNS/2	Nominated Supplier Warranty for use with JCT 80
TNT	trinitrotoluene (high explosive)
to	take over (printing)
TO	turn over
tog	together
TOKAMAK	type of magnetic confinement (fusion)
TOP	technical and office profile (computers)
TOPS	Training Opportunities Scheme
TOR	Treaty of Rome
TOVALOP	Tanker Owners Voluntary Agreement concerning Liability for Oil Pollution
TOW	transport on water
TP	tax payer
TP	town planning
TPDC	Trafford Park Development Corporation
TPI	Town Planning Institute (now RTPI)
TPM	total project management
TPO	tree preservation order
TPS	toughened polystyrene
TQ	Torquay (postcode area)
TQM	total quality management
TR	thio rubber, polysulphide rubber
tr	trench
tr	trowelled
TR	Truro, Cornwall (postcode area)
TRADA	Timber Research and Development Association
TRADA QAS	TRADA Quality Assurance Services
trans	transfer
trans	translated
TRC	Telecommunications Research Centre
TRHA	Trent Regional Health Authority
TRIGA	Trigger (nuclear) reactor
Tripartite Committee	Governments and standards bodies of UK, France and Germany
TRL	transistor resistor logic
TRON	The Real-time Operating System Nucleus
TRPB	Tay River Purification Board
TRPB	Tweed River Purification Board
TRRL	Transport and Road Research Laboratory (DTp)
TRS	tough rubber sheathed (cable)

trs	transpose (printing)
TRS-80	a Tandy range of microcomputers
TS	Cleveland (postcode area)
TS	Tourism Society
TSA	Technical Services Agency (Scotland)
TSA	The Survey Association (full name: UK Land and Hydrographic Survey Association)
TSB	Trustee Savings Bank
TSO	trading standards officer
tsp	teaspoon
TSR	terminate and stay resident (computers)
TSS	Technical Standard Services
TSSA	Transport Salaried Staffs Association
TTF	Timber Trade Federation
TTL	transistor transistor logic
TTS	true to scale
TU	trough urinal

TUA	Telecommunications Users Association
TUAC	Trade Union Advisory Committee (OECD)
Tubemasters	BSC Tubes Division
TUC	Trades Union Congress
TUCC	Transport Users Consultative Council
Tues	Tuesday
T unit	trichromatic unit (used in colour matching)
TURU	Trade Union Research Unit
TUS	Technical Unit for Sport (Sports Council)
TV	television
TW	Thames Water (formerly TWA)
TW	Twickenham (postcode area)
TWA	Thames Water Authority (RWA) (now TW)
TWDC	Tyne and Wear Development Corporation
TWL	top water level
TWR	time-weighted rate of return
TWR	Tyne and Wear (BS county code)

U

U	see U-value
U	upper-class
U	uranium (chemical element)
U	urinal
U	Ventilation/Air conditioning systems (Common Arrangement)
UA	unit of account (see EUA)
UAE	United Arab Emirates
UAR	United Arab Republic (now Arab Republic of Egypt)
UAS	Urban Aid Scheme
UB	Southall, Middlesex (postcode area)
UB	unemployment benefit
UB	universal beam
UB40	unemployment benefit attendance card
UBED	unexpended balance of established development value

UBIC	Unified Building Industry Classification (feasibility study 1990)
UBM	United Builders Merchants
UBR	uniform business rate
u/c	undercoat
UC	universal column
uc	upper case (printing)
UCATT	Union of Construction, Allied Trades and Technicians
UCCA	Universities Central Council on Admissions
UCG	underground coal gasification
UCITS	Undertaking for Collective Investment in Transferable Securities (EC)
UCL	University College London
UCO	Use Classes Order
UCSD p-System	an operating system for Pascal programs (computers)

UCW	Union of Communication Workers	ULCC	ultra large crude carriers (oil)
		ult	*ultimo* (Lat: of or in last month)
UD	*ut dictum* (Lat: as directed)	UMIST	University of Manchester Institute of Science and Technology
UDC	Universal Decimal Classification		
UDC	urban district council (pre-1974)		
UDG	Urban Design Group	UMT	ultrasonic measurement technology
UDL	uniformly distributed load		
UDO	Universal Drawing Office	UN	Unified (screw thread designation system)
UDP	unitary development plan		
		UN	United Nations
UEAtc	European Union of Agrément	UNA	United Nations Association
UER	university entry requirement	UNAC	UN Africa Council
		UNADA	UN Atomic Develpment Authority
UF	urea, urea-formaldehyde		
UFC	University Funding Council (successor to UGC)	UNC	Unified coarse (screw thread)
		UNCAST	UN Conference on the Applications of Science and Technology
UFP	University for Peace (UN)		
U-gauge	U-shaped water gauge used in air tests on drains and gas pipes		
		UNCDF	UN Capital Development Fund
UGC	University Grants Committee (superseded by UFC)	UNCHS	UN Centre for Human Settlements
		UNCLOS	UN Conference on the Law of the Sea
UGP	unglazed pipe		
		UNCNRET	UN Centre for Natural Resources Energy and Transport
UHF	ultra high frequency		
UHT	ultra high temperature	UNCSTD	UN Conference on Science and Technology for Development
UIA	Union Internationale des Architectes		
		UNCTAD	UN Conference on Trade and Development
UICB	Union Internationale des Centres du Batiment (= IUBC)		
		UNDP	UN Development Programme
UIP	unfair industrial practice	UNDRO	UN Disaster Relief Organisation
		UNECA	UN Economic Committee for Africa
UK	United Kingdom		
UKAAA	UK Architects Against Apartheid	UNEP	UN Environmental Programme
UKAEA	UK Atomic Energy Authority	UNESCO	UN Educational, Scientific and Cultural Organisation
UKAPE	UK Association of Professional Engineers		
		UNETAS	UN Emergency Technical Aid Service
UK CARES	UK Certification Authority for Reinforcing Steels		
		UNF	Unified fine (screw thread designation system)
UKEA	UK Energy Authority		
UK-ISES	International Solar Energy Society – UK Section	UNFAD	UN Fund for Agricultural Development
		UNFAO	UN Food and Agricultural Organisation
UKITO	UK Information Technology Organisation		
UKLHSA	UK Land and Hydrographic Survey Association (aka TSA)	UNFPA	UN Population Fund (formerly UN Fund for Population Activities – acronym retained)
UKMWA	UK Mineral Wool Association (aka Eurisol UK)		
		UNFSTD	UN Fund for Science and Technology for Development
UKREP	Office of the UK Representative to the European Communities		
		UNGA	UN General Assembly
UKWFBS	UK Water Fittings Byelaws Scheme	UNHQ	UN Headquarters (New York)
		UNIC	UN Information Centre
		UNICE	Conference of Industries of the European Communities
ULA	uncommitted logic array (computers)		
		UNICEF	UN Children's Fund

UNIDO	UN Industrial Development Organisation
UNIO	UN Information Organisation
UNIPEDE	International Union of Producers and Distributors of Electrical Energy
UNISIST	Universal System for Information in Science and Technology
UNITAR	UN Institute for Training and Research
Univ	university
UNIVAC	Universal Automatic Computer (1951)
UNIX	a multi-user operating system (computers)
UNO	United Nations Organisation
UNRISD	UN Research Institute for Social Development
UNRRA	UN Relief and Rehabilitation Administration
UNRWA	UN Relief and Works Agency
UNSCEAR	UN Scientific Committee on Effects of Atomic Radiation
UNTAA	UN Technical Assistance Administration
UNTAB	UN Technical Assistance Board
UNU	UN University
UNWRA	UN Works and Relief Agency
UP	polyester, unsaturated polyester
UPPED	Use of Personal Protective Equipment Directive (EC)
UPRN	unique property reference number
UPS	uninterrupted power supply
UPU	Universal Postal Union (UN)
uPVC	unplasticised PVC
URBALINE	on-line database: urban and local government issues
URG	urban regeneration grant
URPI	Unit of Retail Planning Information
URTU	United Road Transport Union
US	Ulster Society (for the preservation of the countryside)
u/s	underside
U/S	unserviceable, useless
USA	United States of America
USAID	United States Agency for International Development
USER	Urban Social Environmental Research (Hunt Thompson Associates)
USM	Unlisted Securities Market
USSR	Union of Soviet Socialist Republics
USW	ultrasonic waves
UTC	Co-ordinated Universal Time (has replaced GMT in scientific work)
UUG	Unigraphics User Group (computers)
UV	ultra-violet
U-value	thermal transmittance
UWCC	University of Wales College of Cardiff
UWED	Use of Work Equipment Directive (EC)
UWIST	University of Wales Institute of Science and Technology

---

V

V	5 (Roman numeral)
V̄	5000 (Roman numeral)
V	Electrical supply/power/lighting systems (Common Arrangement)
V	electric potential
v	frequency
V	vanadium (chemical element)
v	velocity
v	*versus* (Lat: against)
v	very
V	victory
v	*vide* (Lat: see)
V	volt (unit of electric potential)
V, v	volume
Vac	vacant
vac	vacuum
vacvac	double vacuum (timber preservation process)
VADS	value-added data services
V&A	Victoria and Albert Museum
VANS	value-added network services

VAR	value-added reseller		VIR	vulcanised india-rubber
VAR	visual-aerial radio range		vis-a-vis	in relation to
VASCAR	electronic device for timing traffic speed		vit	vitreous
			viz	*videlicet* (Lat: that is to say)
VAT	value-added tax		VLBI	very long base interformetry (surveying – OS)
VATTR	*Value Added Tax Tribunal Reports*			
VAV	variable air volume (air-conditioning system)		VLF	very low frequency
			VLSI	very large scale integration (computers)
VC	vice-chairman			
VC	Victoria Cross		VM	value management (same as VE)
VCCT	valuation and community charge tribunal		VMS	voice messaging system (telecommunications)
VCOAD	Voluntary Committee on Overseas Aid and Development		VO	variation order
			VO	verbal order
VCPOL	Vienna Convention for the Protection of the Ozone Layer		vol	volume
VCR	video cassette recorder		VP	vacant possession
			VP	vanishing point
VDT	visual display terminal		VP	vent (ventilation) pipe
VDU	visual display unit		VP	Vice-President
			VPS	vacuum extruded polystyrene
VE	value engineering		VPS	visual programme system
VEB	volkseigener betrieb (Ger: public company)		VRC	visible-record computer
VED	vehicle excise duty		VRI	vulcanised rubber insulated (cable)
VEDC	Vitreous Enamel Development Council		VRM	variable rate mortgage
vent	ventilation, ventilator			
VERA	vision electronic recording apparatus		VS	Victorian Society
			VS	viscosity grades (ISO)
vert	vertical		VSO	Voluntary Service Overseas
			VSOP	vast surpluses of the oil producers
VG	very good			
VGA	video graphics array		VT	virtual terminal (computers)
VGS	visual guidance system (CAD)		VTOC	volume table of contents (computers)
VHF	very high frequency		VTOL	vertical take-off and landing
VHS	vertical helical scanning (a system for reading information from video tape)		VTR	video tape recorder
			VVO	very very old
VIP	very important person			
VIP	visual information processor		VWT	Vincent Wildlife Trust

W

W	Communications/Security/Control systems (Common Arrangement)		W	London Western (postcode area)
			W	tungsten (alternative name wolfram – chemical element)
W	load (mechanical)		W	Wales

W	watt (unit of power)
W	Wednesday
W	weight
W	west
W	width
W	window
W	woman, women
W, w	work
WA	Warrington (postcode area)
WAA	Water Authorities Association
WAC	Welsh Arts Council
WACTC	Welsh Association of Communities and Town Councils
WAES	Workshop on Alternative Energy Strategy
WAG	Women Architects Group
WAN	wide area network (computers)
W&VP	waste and vent pipe
WAQ	with approximate quantities
WAR	Warwickshire (BS county code)
WAR	Westminster Association of Residents
WARM	Warm – The Real Fire Heating Association (formerly Wood and Solid Fuel Association of Retailers and Manufacturers)
Warsaw Pact	The Warsaw Treaty of Friendship, Co-operation and Mutual Assistance (USSR and satellites)
WB	wash basin
Wb	weber (unit of magnetic flux)
WB	World Bank (IBRD)
WBP	weather and boil proof (plywood)
WC	London Western Central (postcode area)
WC	water closet
WC	water company
w/c	week commencing
WC	World Court (UN)
WCA	Water Companies Association
WCAP	World Climate Applications Programme (WMO)
WCC	Welsh Consumer Council
WCD	with contractor's design
WCD 81	Standard Form of Building Contract with Contractor's Design 1981 (JCT)
WCDP	World Climate Data Programme (WMO)
WCE	Watt Committee on Energy
WCIP	World Climate Impact Studies Programme (WMO)
WCL	World Conference of Labour

WCMC	World Conservation Monitoring Centre
WCP	World Climate Programme (WMO)
WCRP	World Climate Research Programme (WMO)
WCSPC	West Country Strategic Planning Conference
WD	Watford (postcode area)
WD	working drawing
WD	Workplace Directive (EC)
WDA	Welsh Development Agency
WDG	Waterloo Development Group
WDM	World Development Movement
wdw	window
w/e	week ending
WEA	Western European Union
Wed	Wednesday
WEDWC	Wrexham and East Denbighshire Water Company
WEEP	Work Experience on Employer's Premises (MSC)
wef	with effect from
WELABCC	West of England Local Authorities Building Control Consortium
WEN	Women's Environmental Network
WES	Women's Engineering Society
Wet	nickname for Excluded Sectors Directive, covering public procurement in water, energy, transport and telecommunications sectors (EC)
WF	Wakefield, West Yorkshire (postcode area)
wf	wrong fount (printing)
WFBS	Water Fittings Byelaws Scheme (Water Research Centre)
WFRC	Warrington Fire Research Centre
WFTU	World Federation of Trade Unions
WG	white glazed
wg	wire guage
WGC	Welwyn Garden City
WGECL	Working Group on European Community Liaison
WGIBC	Working Group on Indices for Building Contracts (DOE)
WGICEC	Working Group on Indices for Civil Engineering Contracts (DOE)
WGM	West Glamorgan (BS county code)

WHCSA	Welsh Health Common Services Authority
WHO	World Health Organisation (UN)
WHSSB	Western Health and Social Services Board (Northern Ireland)
WHTSO	Welsh Health Technical Services Organisation
WHWC	West Hampshire Water Company
WI	Welding Institute
wi	width
WI	wrought iron
WICS	Water Industry Certification Scheme
WID	West India Docks
WIHB	Western Isles Health Board
WIL	Wiltshire (BS county code)
WILDSCAPE	on-line database: nature conservation, farming and wildlife
WIMP	window, icon, mouse, pull-down menu; or window, icon, menu, pointer (computers)
WIP	work in progress
WIPO	World Intellectual Property Organisation (UN)
WIRA	Wool Industry Research Association
WIS	Western Isles, Scotland (BS county code)
WISE	Women into Science and Engineering
wk	week
wk	work
wkly	weekly
WKS	works contract
WKS1/1	Works Contract Invitation to Tender for use with MC 87
WKS1/2	Works Contract Tender for use with MC 87
WKS1/3	Works Contract Agreement for use with MC 87
WKS2	Works Contract Conditions for use with MC 87
WKS3	Works Contract Employer/Works Contractor Agreement for use with MC 87
WKWC	West Kent Water Company
WL, W/L	wavelength
WLAS	West London Architectural Society (RIBA branch)
WLR	*Weekly Law Reports*
W/M	washing machine
WM	water meter
WMA	Wallcovering Manufacturers Association of Great Britain
WMA	Waterheater Manufacturers Association
WMA	Welding Manufacturers Association
WMAC	Waste Management Advisory Council
WMAC	Water Management Advisory Council
WMBCC	West Midlands Building Control Consortium
WMC	world meteorological centre (WMO)
WMD	West Midlands (BS county code)
WMIB	Waste Management Information Bureau
WMO	World Meteorological Organisation (UN)
WMRF	West Midlands Regional Forum of Strategic Local Authorities
WMRHA	West Midlands Regional Health Authority
WN	*Weekly Notes* (law reports)
WN	Wigan, Lancashire (postcode area)
WNW	west-north-west
WO	War Office
WO	Welsh Office
WOASH	Women Organised Against Sexual Harassment
WOBS	workmanship on building sites (BS 8000)
WOCE	World Ocean Circulation Experiment
Wolfson Unit MTIA	Wolfson Unit for Marine Technology and Industrial Aerodynamics
WOQ	without quantities
WORM	write once read many (computers)
WOW	waiting on weather
WP	Warsaw Pact (qv)
WP	waste pipe
WP	weather permitting
WP	without prejudice
WP	word processor/processing
WP	working party
WPB	waste paper basket/bin
WPE	white porcelain enamel
wpm	words per minute
WPWRA	Wallpaper, Paints and Wallcoverings Retailers Association

107

WQ	with quantities	wt	weight
WQS	World Quality System	WT	Woodland Trust
		WTB	Wales Tourist Board
WR	weather resistant (steel)		
WR	Worcester (postcode area)	WV	Wolverhampton (postcode area)
WRA	Water Research Association		
WRB	Water Resources Board	WW	Welsh Water (formerly WWA)
WRC	Water Research Centre	WW	Wessex Water (formerly WWA)
WRC	Water Resource Council	WW1	first world war
WRCWFBS	Water Research Centre Water Fittings Bylaws Scheme	WW2	second world war
WRDC	Warrington and Runcorn Development Corporation	WWA	Welsh Water Authority (RWA) (now WW)
WRHA	Wessex Regional Health Authority	WWA	Wessex Water Authority (RWA) (now WW)
wrot	wrought (of timber)	WWF	World Wide Fund for Nature
		WWP	waste water preventor
WS	Walsall (postcode area)	WWPA	Western Wood Products Association (USA)
WS	work section	WWSMA	Wood Wool Slab Manufacturers
WS	Writer to the Signet		Association
WSA	Wolverhampton Society of Architects (RIBA branch)		
WSA	Worcestershire Society of Architects (RIBA branch)	WYHETSJC	West Yorkshire Highways, Engineering and Technical Services Joint Committee
WSFARM	see WARM	WYK	West Yorkshire (BS county code)
WSFC	Women's Solid Fuel Council	WYSIWYG	what you see is what you get (computers)
WSL	Warren Spring Laboratory (DTI)		
WSW	west-south-west	WYTLG	West Yorkshire Technical Liaison Group
WSX	West Sussex (BS county code)		

X

X	10 (Roman numeral)	X-mark	face mark (pencil mark to indicate first-prepared face edge of joinery from which other edges are to be measured)
x	extension (telephone number)		
X	point on plan at which stated level applies		
X	Transport systems (Common Arrangement)	Xmas	Christmas
X, x	unknown quantity	XNBR	carboxylic-nitrile-butadiene (rubber)
X chart	chart used in systems analysis, relationships being indicated by Xs	X-rays	electromagnetic radiation lying between UV radiation and gamma rays
Xe	xenon (chemical element)	x-reb	cross rebated
XENIX	an operating system derived from UNIX (computers)	XSBR	carboxylic-styrene-butadiene (rubber)
x-gr	cross grain	x-tngd	cross tongued
XLPE	cross-linked polyethylene	X–Y	two directions at right angles

Y

Y	Services reference specification (Common Arrangement)	YOP	youth opportunities programme
y	year	YP	year's purchase
Y	yttrium (chemical element)	YQAFS	Yarsley Quality Assured Firms Scheme
Yard	New Scotland Yard (police headquarters)	yr	year
YB	year book	YRHA	Yorkshire Regional Health Authority
Yb	ytterbium (chemical element)	yrs	yours
yd	yard	YS	York stone
YE	Yorkshire Electricity	YTC	Yarsley Technical Centre
YG	yard gulley	YT(S)	Youth Training (Scheme)
YHRA	Yorkshire and Humberside Regional Association	YW	Yorkshire Water (RWA)
		YWC	York Water Company
YNYSA	York and North Yorkshire Society of Architects (RIBA branch)	YZ	wise head, as in the YZ Club, for those escaping serious injury through wearing safety helmet (RoSPA)
YO	York (postcode area)		
YOC	Youth Opportunities Commission		

Z

Z	Building fabric reference specification (Common Arrangement)	ZETA	zero energy thermonuclear apparatus
Z	impedance	ZIP	zoning improvement plan (USA postal codes)
Z	zero		
Z-80	a processor chip (computers)	Zn	zinc (chemical element)
ZADCA	Zinc Alloy Die Casters Association	ZPDA	Zinc Pigment Development Association
ZDA	Zinc Development Association	Zr	zirconium (chemical element)
ZE	Lerwick, Shetland (postcode area)		
ZET	Shetland, Scotland (BS county code)	ZZZ	Zzzzzzz

LOLO!

OL!

You what?

If you're not *quite* sure what everyone else is talking about, this might help.

aka	also known as
AWOL	absent without leave
BA	bloody architect
BF	bloody fool
BO	body odour
Dinks	double income no kids
FLOP	functional lapse in operational procedure (air traffic control term for a near miss)
GBH	grievous bodily harm
GOM	grand old man
GRQ	get rich quick
guppie	green or ecologically-aware yuppie
KAB	know-all blighter
KISS	keep it simple, stupid
MCP	male chauvinist pig
MOR	middle of the road
MYOB	mind your own business
NBG	no bloody good
NIMBY	not in my back yard
NMP	not my problem
OTL	out to lunch, useless
OTT	over the top
PDQ	pretty damn quick
POETS	push off early tomorrow's Saturday (so POETS day is Friday)
Poosslqs	persons of opposite sex sharing living quarters
RIBA	remember I'm the bloody architect
SOB	sonofabitch
SWALK	sealed with a loving kiss
TGIF	thank God it's Friday
TLC	tender loving care
TTFN	ta-ta for now
WPB	waste paper basket
YP	your problem
yuppie	young upwardly-mobile person

Part 2

Classified Lists

Chemical elements

A = atomic number
B = symbol
C = name

A	B	C	A	B	C	A	B	C
1	H	hydrogen	38	Sr	strontium	75	Re	rhenium
2	He	helium	39	Y	yttrium	76	Os	osmium
3	Li	lithium	40	Zr	zirconium	77	Ir	iridium
4	Be	beryllium	41	Nb	niobium	78	Pt	platinum
5	B	boron	42	Mo	molybdenum	79	Au	gold
6	C	carbon	43	Tc	technetium	80	Hg	mercury
7	N	nitrogen	44	Ru	ruthenium	81	Tl	thallium
8	O	oxygen	45	Rh	rhodium	82	Pb	lead
9	F	fluorine	46	Pd	palladium	83	Bi	bismuth
10	Ne	neon	47	Ag	silver	84	Po	polonium
11	Na	sodium	48	Cd	cadmium	85	At	astatine
12	Mg	magnesium	49	In	indium	86	Rn	radon
13	Al	aluminium	50	Sn	tin	87	Fr	francium
14	Si	silicon	51	Sb	antimony	88	Ra	radium
15	P	phosphorus	52	Te	tellurium	89	Ac	actinium
16	S	sulfur	53	I	iodine	90	Th	thorium
17	Cl	chlorine	54	Xe	xenon	91	Pa	protactinium
18	Ar	argon	55	Cs	caesium	92	U	uranium
19	K	potassium	56	Ba	barium	93	Np	neptunium
20	Ca	calcium	57	La	lanthanum	94	Pu	plutonium
21	Sc	scandium	58	Ce	cerium	95	Am	americium
22	Ti	titanium	59	Pr	praseodymium	96	Cm	curium
23	V	vanadium	60	Nd	neodymium	97	Bk	berkelium
24	Cr	chromium	61	Pm	promethium	98	Cf	californium
25	Mn	manganese	62	Sm	samarium	99	Es	einsteinium
26	Fe	iron	63	Eu	europium	100	Fm	fermium
27	Co	cobalt	64	Gd	gadolinium	101	Md	Mendelevium
28	Ni	nickel	65	Tb	terbium	102	No	nobelium
29	Cu	copper	66	Dy	dysprosium	103	Lr	lawrencium
30	Zn	zinc	67	Ho	holmium	104	–	unnilquadium
31	Ga	gallium	68	Er	erbium	105	–	unnilpentium
32	Ge	germanium	69	Tm	thulium	106	–	unnilhexium
33	As	arsenic	70	Yb	ytterbium	107	–	unnilseptium
34	Se	selenium	71	Lu	lutetium	108	–	unniloctium
35	Br	bromine	72	Hf	hafnium	109	–	unnilennium
36	Kr	krypton	73	Ta	tantalum			
37	Rb	rubidium	74	W	tungsten			

Common Arrangement

First-level work section groupings. These 24 references and headings should become familiar through daily use in project documentation. Refer to *Common arrangement of work sections for building works* for the full list of work sections and their definitions.

A   Preliminaries/General conditions

B   Complete buildings

C   Demolition/Alteration/Renovation
D   Groundwork

E   Insitu concrete/Large precast concrete
F   Masonry
G   Structural/Carcassing metal/timber
H   Cladding/Covering
J   Waterproofing
K   Linings/Sheathing/Dry partitioning
L   Windows/Doors/Stairs
M   Surface finishes
N   Furniture/Equipment
P   Building fabric sundries

Q   Paving/Planting/Fencing/Site furniture

R   Disposal systems
S   Piped supply systems
T   Mechanical heating/cooling/refrigeration systems
U   Ventilation/Air conditioning systems
V   Electrical supply/power/lighting systems
W   Communications/Security/Control systems
X   Transport systems

Y   Services reference specification
Z   Building fabric reference specification

Computers and telecommunications

1GL	1st generation language (machine code – specific to machine)
2D	2-dimensional (applied to CAD drafting systems)
2GL	2nd generation language (assembler – specific to machine but extended capabilities)
2½D	'2½-dimensional' (applied to 2D CAD drafting systems which can generate elevations and certain 3D projections if heights are input; now obsolete)
3D	3-dimensional (applied to CAD modelling systems)
3GL	3rd generation language (written for variety of machines and then 'compiled' for specific machine)
4GL	4th generation language (3GL Mark 2)
ACARD	Advisory Council for Applied Research and Development
ACC	Association of Computer Clubs
ACCESS	automatic computer controlled electronic scanning system
ACCOMPLINE	on-line database: planning and local government subjects
ACE	Automatic Computing Engine (1950)
ACEA	Association for Computing in Engineering and Architecture
ACRE	automatic call recording equipment
ACS	Applied CAD Services (CAD dealer)
A/D	analogue to digital
ADA	a programming language
ADC	advise dialling charge, advise duration and charge
ADC	automatic digital calculator
ADP	automatic data processing
AEC	architectural, engineering, constructional (CAD software)
AEI	Associated Electrical Industries
AF	audio frequency
AICS	Association of Independent Computer Specialists
ALGOL	algorithmic language (a programming language for scientific applications)
ALU	arithmetic logic unit
AM	amplitude modulation
amp	amplifier
AND	a logic gate
ANSI	American National Standards Institute
AOS	an operating system
A-party	originator of telephone call
APCC	Association of Professional Computer Consultants
APL	a programming language
AQUALINE	on-line database: water resources and supplies
ARQ	automatic request for re-send
ASCC	Automatic Sequence Controlled Calculator (1944)
ASCII	American Standard Code for Information Interchange
ASF	automatic sheet feeder
AUG	Acropolis User Group
AUG	Autocad User Group
B	binary
BABT	British Approvals Board for Telecommunications
BASIC	beginner's all-purpose symbolic instruction code (the most commonly used programming language for non-specialist applications)
baud	unit of data transmission speed: 1 baud = 2 bps (named after Baudot)
BBC	British Broadcasting Corporation
BCD	binary coded decimal
BCS	British Computer Society
BDF	building distribution frame (telecommunications)
BEITA	British Equipment and Information Technology Association (formerly BETA)
BER	bit error rate
BETA	British Equipment Trade Association (now BEITA)
BIM	bit image mode (printing)
bit	binary digit
BITS	BSI Information Technology Services
BLAISE	British Library automated information service
BMMG	British Microcomputer Manufacturers Group
BMS	building management system
BOS	an operating system
B-party	recipient of telephone call
bpi	bits per inch
bps	bits per second
BSC	binary synchronous communications, or bi-synch

BSI	British Standards Institution
BT	British Telecommunications, British Telecom
byte	a unit of, normally, 8 bits
C	a high level language, often associated with UNIX operating system
CAAD	computer-aided architectural design
CACCI	Committee on the Application of Computers in the Construction Industry
CAD	computer-aided design
CADD	computer-aided design and drafting
CADDIA	Co-operation in Automation for Data and Documentation for Import
CAI	common air interface (telecommunications)
CAI	computer-assisted instruction
CAL	computer-assisted learning
CAM	computer-aided manufacture
CAR	computer-aided retrieval
CASE	computer-aided software engineering
CATV	cable television
CBL	computer-based learning
CBM	Commodore Business Machines
CBT	computer-based training
CCC	Chaos Computer Club (Hamburg-based hackers)
CCD	charge coupled device
CCIR	Comité Consultatif International de Radio (ITU)
CCITT	Comité Consultatif International des Telegraphes et Telephones (ITU)
CCL	common command language
CCP	console command processor
CCP/M	a control program (multi-tasking version of CP/M)
CCR	commitment concurrency and recovery
CD	compact disk
CD-E	CD-erasable
CD-R	CD-recordable
CD-ROM	CD – read only memory
CDV	compact disk video
CEEFAX	see facts (BBC televised information system)
CEPT	Conference Européenne des Administrations des Postes et Telecoms
CGA	colour graphics adaptor
CGI	computer graphics interface
CGM	computer graphics metafile
CICA	Construction Industry Computing Association
CIL	Computers in Libraries (annual exhibition and conference; formerly SCIL)
CILE	call information logging equipment
CIMTECH	Centre for Information, Media and Technology
CISS	*Construction Industry Software Selector* (RIBAS)
CLAIMS	Contract Law Advisory and Information Management System (database)
CLT	computer language translator
CMC	caractère magnétique code (magnetic character code)
CMI	computer-managed instruction
CML	computer-managed learning
CMOS	complementary MOS
CMR	cellular mobile radio
coax	coaxial cable
COBOL	common business orientated language
CODASYL	Conference on Data Systems Languages (USA)
codec	coder decoder
COL	computer orientated language
COM	computer output on microfilm
COMAL	a high level programming language
CORAL	a high level programming language
CPETA	Computer and Peripherals Equipment Trade Association
CPM	cards per minute
CP/M	control program for microcomputers; or control, program, monitor
cps	characters per second
CPU	central processing unit
CRT	cathode-ray tube
c/s	cycles per second (unit of frequency, superseded by hertz)
CSA	Computing Services Association
CSDN	circuit switched data network
CSERB	Computer Systems and Electronic Requirements Board
CSITC	Computing Services Industry Training Council
CT	cordless telephone
CT2	cordless telephone, second generation
CUG	Cadam User Group
CUG	Calcomp User Group
CUG	closed user group

CUG	Computervision User Group
CUUG	Caddie UK User Group
C-VIEW	on-line database: general community information
DASD	direct access storage device (IBM new generation of disk drive)
DASS	digital access signalling system
DAT	digital audio tape
Datel	data telecommunications (British Telecom data transmission facility)
DBMS	database management system
DCE	data circuit terminating equipment
DDL	data description language (part of DBMS)
DECT	digital European cordless telephone
DECUS	Digital Equipment Computer Users Society
DEM	Dialcom Electronic Mail
DETAB	a programming language
DIF	data interchange format
DIP	dual inline package
DM	dot matrix (printing)
DMA	direct memory access
DML	data manipulation language (part of DBMS)
DMS	data management system
DOAM	distributed office applications model
DOS	disk operating system, disk-based operating system
DP	data processing
DPA	Data Protection Act
DPC	data protection co-ordinator
dpi	dots per inch
DPNSS	digital private network signalling system
DPR	Data Protection Registrar
DRAM	dynamic random access memory
DRAW	direct read after write
DRI	Digital Research (California) Incorporated
DTE	data terminal equipment
DTL	diode transistor logic
DTP	desktop publishing
DUG	dBase Users Group
DVI	digital video interactive
DXF	data (or drawing) exchange format
E	erlung (unit of telephone traffic: number of calls per hour × average length)
EAN	European article numbering/number (bar code)
EAPROM	electrically alterable programmable ROM
EAROM	electrically alterable ROM
EBCDIC	extended binary coded decimal interchange code
ECL	Elstree Computing Limited
ECMA	European Computer Manufacturers Association
EDI	electronic data interchange
EDICON	Electronic Data Interchange in the Construction Industry
EDIFACT	Electronic Data Interchange for Administration, Commerce and Transport
EDP	electronic data processing
EDS	Electronic Data Systems (American company)
EDS	exchangeable disk storage
EDSAC	Electronic Delay Storage Automatic Computer (1949)
EDTV	extended definition television
EDVAC	Electrical Discrete Variable Automatic Computer (1949)
EEA	Electronic Engineering Association
EEPROM	electronically erasable programmable ROM
EGA	enhanced graphics adaptor (improved version of CGA)
EHF	extremely high frequency
EIA	Electronic Industries Association (USA)
EISA	extended industry standard architecture
ELF	extremely low frequency
ELSI	extra large scale integration
em	electromagnetic
Email	electronic mail
EMI	electromagnetic interference
EMS	energy management system (by computer)
ENDOC	on-line database: listing of environmental information and documentation centres in member states of EC
ENIAC	Electronic Numerical Integrator and Calculator (1946 – first electronic computer)
ENREP	on-line database: information on environmental research projects in EC
EPROM	erasable programmable ROM
ERMES	Euromessage (international message paging consortium)
ERNIE	Electronic Random Number Indicator Equipment
EROM	erasable ROM

ESP	environmental system performance (computer program)		GSX	graphics system extension
			GUG	Gable User Group
ESPRIT	European Strategic Research Programme in Information Technology		GUG	GDS User Group
			GUG	Gintran User Group
ETSI	European Telecommunications Standards Institute		HDTV	high definition television
			HOCUS	hand or computer universal simulator (computer system)
EUROKOM	Teleconferencing and Electronic Mail System (ESPRIT)		HUG	Harris User Group
Euronet-Diane			Hz	hertz
	Direct Information Access Network for Europe		IAL	international algebraic language
EVAC	emergency visual audio control		IAR	instruction address register
EVIT	emergency video intelligent terminal		IAS	immediate-access store
			IBA	Independent Broadcasting Authority
EVP	electronic voice phenomena		IBG	inter-block gap
			IBM	International Business Machines Corporation
FACE	International Federation of Computer Users in Engineering, Architecture and related fields		IC	integrated circuit
			ICL	International Computers Limited
FAST	Federation Against Software Theft		ICPUG	Independent Commodore Products Users Group
FAT	file allocation table		ICSTIS	Independent Committee for the Supervision of Television Information Services
fax	facsimile			
FDM	frequency-division multiplexing			
FEDCAD	Federation of CAD User Groups		ICT	International Computers and Tabulators
FET	field effect transistor			
FIFO	first in first out (electronic mail)		IDC	International Data Corporation
FM	frequency modulation		IDD	international direct dialling
FORTH	a high level programming language designed for small computers		IDN	integrated digital network (telecommunications)
			IDP	integrated data processing
FORTRAN	formula translation (a programming language for scientific applications)		IDPM	Institute of Data Processing Management
			IDTV	improved definition television
FOTS	fibre optics transmission system		IEC	International Electrotechnical Commission
Frontiers	forecasting rain optimised using new techniques of interactively enhanced radar and satellite data (MO)		IEE	Institution of Electrical Engineers
			IEEE	a standard interface (IEEE)
			IEEE	Institute of Electrical and Electronics Engineers (USA)
FTAM	file transfer, access and management		IERE	Institution of Electronic and Radio Engineers
			IF	intermediate frequency
GDS	graphics design system (CAD system)		IFIP	International Federation for Information Processing
GEM	graphic environment manager (DRI system)		IFPI	International Federation of Phonogram and Videogram Producers
GIGO	garbage in garbage out			
GKS	graphical kernal system		IGES	initial graphic exchange specification
GOSIP	Government OSI Profile			
GPCSA	General Practice Computer Suppliers Association		IIC	International Institute of Communications
GRACE	graphic arts composing equipment		IN	intelligent network
GSLB	Group Special Large Bands (communications working group)		INDECS	interactive design of control systems

Intel	integrated electronics (American microcomputer manufacturer)	LEO	Lyons Electronic Office (1953 – first office computer)
INTELSAT	International Telecommunications Satellite Consortium	LF	low frequency
		LIFO	last in first out (electronic mail)
I/O	input and output	LISP	list processing language
IP	information provider	lpi	lines per inch
IPUG	IBM PC User Group	lpm	lines per minute
IR	infra-red	LSE	Language Symbolique d'Enseignement (high level computer language)
IRDS	information resource dictionary system		
IS	input system	LSI	large-scale integration
ISBN	international standard book number	LW	long wave
ISDN	integrated services digital network (telecommunications)	M	megabyte
		M	mega (multiple prefix: 10^6 or 1 000 000; but 2^{20} or 1 048 576 in computer storage locations)
ISO	International Organisation for Standardisation		
IT	information technology	MAN	metropolitan area network
ITAP	Information Technology Advisory Panel	MAP	manufacturing automation profile
ITS	Information Thru Speech (American microcomputer for the blind, with voice synthesiser and interconnected brailler)	MAP	Microprocessor Applications Project (DTI)
		MAPCON	MAP Consultants (part of MAP scheme)
ITTTF	Information Technology and Telecommunications Task Force (EC)	MARI	Microelectronics Application Research Institute
		MB	megabyte
		mbps	megabits per second
ITU	International Telecommunications Union (UN)	MCA	micro channel architecture (IBM technology)
ITY	Information Technology Year (1982)	MENTOR	a CBL system
		MF	medium frequency
IUG	Intergraph User Group	MHS	message-handling system (same as electronic mail)
JCL	job control language	MICR	magnetic ink character recognition
JTC	joint technical committee (ISO + IEC)		
		MIS	management information system
JTC1	JTC on information technology standards activities	MISP	microelectronics industry support programme
JTM	job transfer and manipulation	MMI	man machine interface
		modem	modulator/demodulator
K	kilobyte	MOS	metal oxide semiconductor
k	kilo (multiple prefix: 10^3 or 1000)	MOSFET	MOS field effect transistor
K	kilo (multiple prefix for computer storage locations: 2^{10} or 1024)	MOTIS	message-orientated text interchange system
		MPA	multi-user project access (t^2 Solutions software)
KB	kilobyte		
kbps	kilobits per second	MPC	multi-project chip (Australian silicon chip)
LAMSAC	Local Authorities Management Services and Computer Committee	MPCN	Mercury Personal Communications Networks
		MP/M	a control program (multi-user version of CP/M)
LAMUG	Local Authority Micro-Computer User Group		
		MPU	microprocessor unit
LAN	local area network	MS	Microsoft
LCD	liquid-crystal display	MS-DOS	Microsoft disk operating system
LECHRA	housing subsidy computer (DOE)	MSI	medium-scale integration
LED	light-emitting diode		

MSX	a Japanese/American software and hardware standard
MTBF	mean time between failures
MTTR	mean time to repair
MUG	Moss User Group
NAND	not AND (a logic gate)
NCC	National Computing Centre
NEQ	non-equivalence (a logic gate)
NLQ	near letter quality (printing)
NOR	not OR (a logic gate)
NOT	not (a logic gate)
NUI	network user identifier
NWP	numerical weather prediction (by computer)
OA	office automation
OCR	optical character recognition
ODA	office document architecture
ODP	open distributed processing
ODPR	Office of the Data Protection Registrar
OEDIPUS	Oxford English Dictionary integrating, proofing and updating system
OEM	original equipment manufacturer
Oftel	Office of Telecommunications
OIS	office information system
OMR	optical mark reading
ONP	open network provision
OPAC	on-line public access catalogue
OPAMP	operational amplifier
OP-CODE	operational code
OPM	optically projected map
OR	or (a logic gate)
ORACLE	optional reception of announcements by coded line electronics (ITV television newspaper)
OS/2	an IBM operating system
OSI	open systems interconnection (ISO)
PA	personal architect (ECL program)
PA	public address
PABX	private automatic branch exchange
PAL	phase alternation line (a colour TV system)
PAS	public address system
PASCAL	a high level programming language (after Blaise Pascal, who built first mechanical calculator in 1642)
PAX	private automatic exchange
PBX	private branch exchange
PC	personal computer

PCB	printed circuit board
PC-DOS	a disk operating system (MS-DOS adapted for IBM computer)
PCN	personal communications network
PCW	personal computer and word processor
PDN	public data network
PDS	Philips Data Systems
PERINORM	on-line database: European bibliographic standards information produced by BSI, AFNOR and DIN
PERT	programme evaluation and review technique
PET	Personal Electronic Transactor (CBM microcomputer)
PGM	personal ground modeller (ECL program)
PICA	PSA Information on Construction and Architecture
PICK	a multi-user operating system
PILOT	a programming language for creating CAL packages
PIO	programmable input and output
PIP	peripheral interchange program
PIXEL	picture element (one of the dots which make up a screen image)
PL/1	programming language 1 (a high-level programming language)
PLAN	programming language nineteen hundred series (ICL)
PLANEX	on-line database: community planning and related subjects
PLATO	a CBL system
PL/M	programming language for microprocessors
PMS	Project Management Shop
POTS	plain old telephone system
ppm	pages per minute
PROM	programmable ROM
PS/2	an IBM range of personal computers
PSD	personal site designer (ECL program)
PSS	packet switched service, packet switch stream (BT – electronic mail)
PSTN	public switched telephone network
P-System	an operating system
PTT	postal, telegraph and telephone authority (Europe and elsewhere)
PUG	Pafec User Group
PVC	permanent virtual circuit
PVS	Pascal validation suite
PX	private exchange

QUADRO2	queues and delays at roadworks (DoT computer model)
QWERTY	the normal typewriter keyboard (the first six letters)
RAM	random access memory
RDA	remote database access
RDOS	a disk operating system
RF	radio frequency
RGB	red, green, blue
RISC	reduced instruction set computer
RJE	remote job entry
ROM	read only memory
RP	report program generator (a business programming language)
RS232	a standard serial interface for PCs
RSA	response selection amplifier
RSI	repetitive stress injury
RS series	recommendations on data transmission (IEEE)
RTL	resistor transistor logic
RUCAPS	really useful computer-aided production system (originally Riyadh University . . .) (CAD system)
RUG	Robocom User Group
RUG	Rucaps User Group
S100	a standard bus
SAA	system application architecture
SAM	a CBL system
SCMS	serial copy management system (to prevent copies of copies of CDs)
SCIL	Small Computers in Libraries (annual exhibition and conference; now just CIL)
SGML	standard generalised markup language
SHF	super high frequency
SITM	Society of Information Technology Managers
SMATV	satellite master antenna television
SMT	surface mount technology
SNA	system network architecture (IBM version of OSI)
SNARF	systematic numerical analysis of the risk of fire (computerised modelling technique)
SNR	signal-to-noise ratio
SOM	start of message
SONET	synchronous optical network
SOS	silicon on sapphire
SPC	stored program control
SPOOL	simultaneous peripheral operation on-line

SQUID	superconducting quantum interference device
SSI	small-scale integration
STD	subscriber trunk dialling
STEP	Standard for the Exchange of Product Model Data (ISO)
STRAD	signal transmitting receiving and distributing
STX	start of text
t^2	the product of teamwork and technology (t^2 Solutions, formerly GMW Computers)
TACS	total access communications system
TCU	transmission control unit
TDM	time-division multiplexing
TEA	tunnel emission amplifier
TED	Tenders Electronic Daily (EC on-line databank)
TEMA	Telecommunication Engineering and Manufacturing Association
TMA	Telecommunications Managers Association
TOP	technical and office profile
TRC	Telecommunications Research Centre
TRL	transistor resistor logic
TRON	The Real-time Operating System Nucleus
TRS-80	a Tandy range of microcomputers
TTL	transistor transistor logic
TUA	Telecommunications Users Association
TV	television
UCSD p-System	an operating system designed for running Pascal programs
UHF	ultra high frequency
UKITO	UK Information Technology Organisation
ULA	uncommitted logic array
UNIVAC	Universal Automatic Computer (1951)
UNIX	a multi-user operating system
UPS	uninterrupted power supply
URBALINE	on-line database: urban and local government issues
USW	ultrasonic waves
UUG	Unigraphics User Group
UV	ultra-violet
VADS	value-added data services
VANS	value-added network services
VAR	visual-aerial radio range

123

VASCAR	electronic device for timing traffic speed
VDT	visual display terminal
VDU	visual display unit
VERA	vision electronic recording apparatus
VGA	video graphics array
VGS	visual guidance system (CAD)
VHF	very high frequency
VIP	visual information processor
VLF	very low frequency
VLSI	very large scale integration
VMS	voice messaging system
VPS	visual programme system
VRC	visible-record computer
VT	virtual terminal
VTOC	volume table of contents
VTR	video tape recorder
WAN	wide area network

WILDSCAPE	on-line database: nature conservation, farming and wildlife
WIMP	window, icon, mouse, pull-down-menu; or window, icon, menu, pointer
WL, W/L	wavelength
WORM	write once read many
WP	word processor
WYSIWYG	what you see is what you get
X chart	chart used in systems analysis, relationships being indicated by Xs
XENIX	an operating system derived from UNIX
X-Y	two directions at right angles
Z-80	a processor chip

T42

Contracts

A wide range of forms of building contract has been developed, some requiring the use of related documents. This list summarises the main contract and sub-contract forms published by professional and other official bodies.

ISSUING BODIES

ACA	Association of Consultant Architects
ASI	Architects and Surveyors Institute (formerly FAS: Faculty of Architects and Surveyors)
BEC	Building Employers Confederation
BPF	British Property Federation
CASEC	Confederation of Associations of Specialist Engineering Contractors
DOE	Department of the Environment
FIDIC	Fédération Internationale des Ingénieurs Conseils
ICE	Institution of Civil Engineers
JCLI	Joint Council for Landscape Industries
JCT	Joint Contracts Tribunal
RIBA	Royal Institute of British Architects
SBCC	Scottish Building Contract Committee

CONTRACT FORMS

ISSUING BODY	FULL NAME OF DOCUMENT	COMMON ABBREVIATION
ACA	The ACA Form of Building Agreement (1984) The ACA Form of Sub-contract	ACA Form
ACA/BPF	The ACA Form of Building Agreement (1984): BPF edition	ACA/BPF Form
ASI	ASI Building Contract (1986 Edition) ASI Small Works Contract (1981 Edition) ASI Minor Works Contract (1980 Edition) ASI Sub-contract (1981 Edition)	ASI Form (formerly FAS Form)
BEC	Standard form for nominated subcontractors (pre-1980) Standard form for non-nominated subcontractors (pre-1980)	Green Form Blue Form
	Domestic Sub-contract for use with JCT 80 Domestic Sub-contract for use with CD 81 Domestic Sub-contract for use with IFC 84	DOM/1 DOM/2 IN/SC
	Government Works Sub-contract for use with GC/Works/1	GW/S
DOE	Form GC/Works/1, Edition 3: The General Conditions of Contract for Building and Civil Engineering	GC/WKS/1
	Form GC/Works/2: The General Conditions of Government Contracts for Building and Civil Engineering Minor Works	GC/WKS/2

Contracts

FIDIC	FIDIC Conditions of Contract for Works of Civil Engineering Construction	
ICE	Conditions of Contract and Forms of Tender, Agreement and Bond for use in connection with Works of Civil Engineering Construction	ICE Conditions
	Conditions of Contract for Minor Works	ICE Minor Works
JCLI	Form of Agreement for Landscape Works	JCLI Agreement
	JCLI Supplement to the JCT Intermediate Form IFC 84	
JCT	Standard Form of Building Contract 1980 Edition	JCT 80 or SF 80
	Nominated Sub-Contractor documents for use with JCT 80:	
	Tender	NSC/1 or 1a
	Agreement	NSC/2 or 2a
	Nomination	NSC/3 or 3a
	Nominated Sub-Contract	NSC/4 or 4a
	Nominated Supplier documents for use with JCT 80:	
	Tender	TNS/1
	Warranty	TNS/2
	Fixed Fee Form of Prime Cost Contract 1967	
	Standard Form of Building Contract with Contractor's Design 1981 Edition	CD 81
	Standard Form of Management Contract 1987 Edition	MC 87
	Standard Works Contract	WKS1, 2, and 3
	Intermediate Form of Building Contract 1984 Edition	IFC 84
	Named sub-contractor documents for use with IFC 84	
	Tender and Agreement	NAM/T
	Sub-Contract Conditions	NAM/SC
	Agreement for Minor Building Works 1980 Edition	MW 80
	Standard Form of Measured Term Contract 1989 Edition	MTC 89
	Standard Form of Tender and Agreement for Building Works of a Jobbing Character	JA/T 90
	Conditions of Contract for Building Works of a Jobbing Character	JA/C 90
RIBA/CASEC	Named sub-contractor document for use with IFC 84:	
	Form of Employer/Specialist Agreement	ESA/1
SBCC	Scottish Supplement to JCT 80	
	Scottish Supplement to JCT 81 with Contractor's Design	
	Scottish Management Contract 1988	
	Scottish Minor Works Contract 1987	
	Scottish Minor Works Sub-Contract 1987	

126

Counties

Standard 3-letter codes for the names of counties and similar areas in the United Kingdom, from BS 6879. The full standard includes additional 3-letter codes for historic names (eg Rutland), as well as 2-letter and 4-digit codes for current names only. The codes are intended for databases and other records.

England: counties

Avon	AVN
Bedfordshire	BDF
Berkshire	BRK
Buckinghamshire	BKM
Cambridgeshire	CAM
Cheshire	CHS
Cleveland	CLV
Cornwall	CON
Cumbria	CMA
Derbyshire	DBY
Devon	DEV
Dorset	DOR
Durham	DUR
East Sussex	ESX
Essex	ESS
Gloucestershire	GRS
Greater Manchester	GTM
Hampshire	HAM
Hereford and Worcester	HWR
Hertfordshire	HRT
Humberside	HUM
Isle of Wight	IOW
Kent	KEN
Lancashire	LAN
Leicestershire	LEC
Lincolnshire	LIN
Merseyside	MSY
Norfolk	NFK
Northamptonshire	NTH
Northumberland	NBL
North Yorkshire	NYK
Nottinghamshire	NTT
Oxfordshire	OXF
Shropshire	SHR
Somerset	SOM
South Yorkshire	SYK
Staffordshire	STS
Suffolk	SFK
Surrey	SRY
Tyne and Wear	TWR
Warwickshire	WAR
West Midlands	WMD
West Sussex	WSX
West Yorkshire	WYK
Wiltshire	WIL

Wales: counties

Clwyd	CWD
Dyfed	DFD
Gwent	GNT
Gwynedd	GWN
Mid Glamorgan	MGM
Powys	POW
South Glamorgan	SGM
West Glamorgan	WGM

Scotland: regions and islands

Borders	BOR
Central	CEN
Dumfries and Galloway	DGY
Fife	FIF
Grampian	GMP
Highland	HLD
Lothian	LTN
Orkney	ORK
Shetland	ZET
Strathclyde	STD
Tayside	TAY
Western Isles	WIS

Northern Ireland: districts

Antrim	ANT
Ards	ARD
Armagh	ARM
Ballymena	BLA
Ballymoney	BLY
Banbridge	BNB
Belfast	BFS
Carrickfergus	CKF
Castlereagh	CSR
Coleraine	CLR
Cookstown	CKT
Craigavon	CGV
Down	DOW
Dungannon	DGN
Fermanagh	FER
Larne	LRN
Limavady	LMV
Lisburn	LSB
Londonderry	LDY
Magherafelt	MFT
Moyle	MYL
Newry and Mourne	NYM
Newtownabbey	NTA
North Down	NDN
Omagh	OMH
Strabane	STB

The Islands

Guernsey	GSY
Isle of Man	IOM
Isles of Scilly	IOS
Jersey	JSY

Europe

The UK is part of Europe and closely affected by decisions made in Brussels and elsewhere, but the proliferation of organisations is bewildering. This list gives a selection of bodies and activities and a rough indication of their relationships. See also Standards organisations.

COUNCIL OF EUROPE (CE)

Foundation: May 1949

Members (22)

Austria, Belgium, Cyprus, Denmark, France, Greece, Iceland, Ireland, Italy, Liechtenstein, Luxembourg, Malta, Netherlands, Norway, Portugal, San Marino, Spain, Sweden, Switzerland, Turkey, United Kingdom, West Germany

Organisation

Committee of Ministers (principal organ)
Conferences of specialised ministers
Ministers' Deputies
  Parliamentary Assembly
  Standing Committee
  Ordinary Committees
  Secretariat

Activities

CCAHE	Convention for the Conservation of the Architectural Heritage of Europe
CCC	Council for Cultural Co-operation
CCEWNH	Convention on the Conservation of European Wildlife and Natural Habitats
CERF	Council of Europe Resettlement Fund
CSP	Convention on Soil Protection
ECC	European Campaign for the Countryside
ECHR	European Commission on Human Rights
ECHR	European Court of Human Rights
ECLSMW	European Convention on the Legal Status of Migrant Workers
ECS	European Conservation Strategy
ECSS	European Code of Social Security
ECSS	European Convention on Social Security
EPC	European Population Committee
ESC	European Social Charter
SCCMENH	Steering Committee for the Conservation and Management of the Environment and Natural Habitats

	EWC	European Water Charter
	SC	Soil Charter

SCICHH	Steering Committee for Integrated Conservation of the Historic Heritage
SCRMM	Steering Committee on Regional and Municipal Matters

EUROPEAN COMMUNITY (EC)

Composition
Comprises three separate communities:

ECSC	European Coal and Steel Community (Treaty of Paris 18.4.51, effective 25.7.52)
EEC	European Economic Community (Treaty of Rome 25.3.57, effective 1.1.58)
EURATOM	European Atomic Energy Community (dates as EEC)

Now regarded as single entity; supervised by single Commission (CEC) (treaty 8.4.65, effective 1.7.67)

Members (12)
Belgium, Denmark, France, Greece, Ireland, Italy, Luxemburg, Netherlands, Portugal, Spain, United Kingdom, West Germany

Commission of the European Communities (CEC)
Directorates-General (23)

DG III	Internal market and industrial affairs
DG IV	Competition
DG VI	Agriculture
DG VII	Transport
DG VIII	Development
DG X	Information, communication and culture
DG XI	Environment, consumer protection and nuclear safety
DG XII	Science, research and development
DG XIII	Telecommunications, information and innovation
DG XVI	Regional policy
DG XVII	Energy
DG XXIII	Enterprise policy, distributive trades, social economy and tourism

Secretariat-General of the Commission
Legal Service
Statistical Office

EUROSTAT	Statistical Office of the European Communities

Consultative bodies

ECC	ECSC Consultative Committee
ECOSOC	Economic and Social Committee

European Council (EC)
Heads of state or government

Council of Ministers of the European Communities (CMEC)

COREPER	Committee of Permanent Representatives
UKREP	Office of the UK Representative to the European Communities
SCMS	Standing Committee of Member States' Representatives
Secretariat	

European Parliament (EP)

MEP	Member of the European Parliament

Court of Justice of the European Communities

CFI	Court of First Instance
ECJ	European Court of Justice

European Investment Bank (EIB)

Special funds

EAGGF	European Agricultural Guidance and Guarantee Fund
ERDF	European Regional Development Fund
ESF	European Social Fund

Activities

Agriculture

CAP	Common Agricultural Policy
MCAs	monetary compensation amounts

Consumer protection

CCC	Community Consumer Council
CCC	Consumers Consultative Committee
CPG	Consumer Protection Group
CPP	Consumer Protection Programme

Development

EAC	European Association for Co-operation

Economic and monetary union

CEEC	European Committee of Construction Economists
ECU	European Currency Unit
EMCF	European Monetary Co-operation Fund
EMS	European Monetary System
EMU	Economic and Monetary Union
EUA	European Unit of Account (replaced by ECU in 1981)

Education and culture

COMETT	Programme of education and training for technology
ERASMUS	European Action Scheme for the Mobility of University Students
EURYDICE	Education Information Network in the European Community

Energy

ITER	International Thermonuclear Experimental Reactor
JET	Joint European Torus (nuclear energy programme)
JOULE	Joint Opportunities for Unconverted or Long Term Energy Supply
NET	Next European Torus

Environmental policy

VCPOL	Vienna Convention for the Protection of the Ozone Layer

Fisheries

CFP	Common Fisheries Policy

Industry

BRITE	Basic Research in Industrial Technologies for Europe

Science and technology

DIANE	Direct Information Access Network
EIDS	European Innovation Diagnosis Scheme
ENBRI	European Network of Building Research Institutes
ESPRIT	European Strategic Research Programme in Information Technology
EURAM	European Research in Advanced Materials
EUREKA	European Research Co-ordination Agency (wider European collaboration in which EC participates)
FAST	Forecasting and Assessment in Science and Technology
IDEA	Innovation Development European Appraisal
JRC	Joint Research Centre
RACE	Research and Development in Advanced Communication Technology in Europe
SPRINT	European Strategic Programme for Innovation and Technology Transfer

Social matters

EFILWC	European Foundation for the Improvement of Living and Working Conditions

Trade
EIC	European information centre
GRIM	Group on Regulations, Information and Management
SEM	Single European Market (SEM Act 1986 set objective of completion of a European internal market by end of 1992)
TFSME	Task Force on Small and Medium-sized Enterprises

Transport
DRIVE	Dedicated Road Safety Systems and Intelligent Vehicles in Europe
ECMT	European Conference of Ministers of Transport

Directives

Selection of directives approved or in draft

AD	Architects' Directive
CD	Compliance Directive
CPD	Construction Products Directive
ECD	Electromagnetic Compatibility Directive
ESD	Excluded Sectors Directive (public procurement in water, energy, transport and telecommunications sectors)
GAD	Gas Appliances Directive
GD	General Directive (professional qualifications not covered by separate directive)
MSD	Machine Safety Directive
PLD	Product Liability Directive
PSD	Public Supplies Directive
PWD	Public Works Directive
UPPED	Use of Personal Protective Equipment (PPE) Directive
UWED	Use of Work Equipment Directive

OTHER ORGANISATIONS

European Free Trade Association (EFTA)

Members (6)

Austria, Finland, Iceland, Norway, Sweden, Switzerland
(Denmark, Portugal and UK, founder members of EFTA, subsequently left and joined EC)

Council for Mutual Economic Assistance (CMEA or COMECON)

Members (10)

Bulgaria, Cuba, Czechoslovakia, East Germany, Hungary, Mongolia, Poland, Romania, USSR, Viet-nam

The Warsaw Treaty of Friendship, Co-operation and Mutual Assistance (The Warsaw Pact)

Members (7)

Bulgaria, Czechoslovakia, East Germany, Hungary, Poland, Romania, USSR

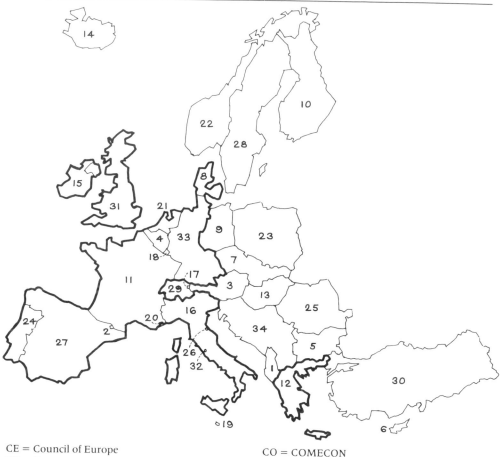

CE = Council of Europe
EC = European Community
EF = EFTA

CO = COMECON
WP = Warsaw Pact

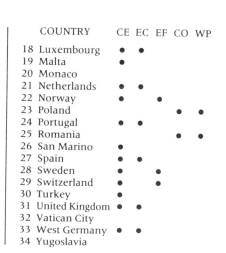

COUNTRY	CE	EC	EF	CO	WP
1 Albania					
2 Andorra					
3 Austria	•		•		
4 Belgium	•	•			
5 Bulgaria				•	•
6 Cyprus	•				
7 Czechoslovakia				•	•
8 Denmark	•	•			
9 East Germany				•	•
10 Finland			•		
11 France	•	•			
12 Greece	•	•			
13 Hungary				•	•
14 Iceland	•		•		
15 Ireland	•	•			
16 Italy	•	•			
17 Liechtenstein	•				

COUNTRY	CE	EC	EF	CO	WP
18 Luxembourg	•	•			
19 Malta	•				
20 Monaco					
21 Netherlands	•	•			
22 Norway	•		•		
23 Poland				•	•
24 Portugal	•		•		
25 Romania				•	•
26 San Marino	•				
27 Spain	•	•			
28 Sweden	•		•		
29 Switzerland	•		•		
30 Turkey	•				
31 United Kingdom	•	•			
32 Vatican City					
33 West Germany	•	•			
34 Yugoslavia					

Greek alphabet

NAME	UPPER CASE	LOWER CASE	ENGLISH EQUIVALENT
Alpha	A	α	a (short)
Beta	B	β	b
Gamma	Γ	γ	g
Delta	Δ	δ	d
Epsilon	E	ε	e (short)
Zeta	Z	ζ	z
Eta	H	η	e (long)
Theta	Θ	θ	th
Iota	I	ι	i (short)
Kappa	K	κ	k
Lambda	Λ	λ	l
Mu	M	μ	m
Nu	N	ν	n
Xi	Ξ	ξ	x
Omicron	O	o	o (long)
Pi	Π	π	p
Rho	P	ρ	r
Sigma	Σ	σ ς	s
Tau	T	τ	t
Upsilon	Y	υ	u (short) or y
Phi	Φ	φ	ph
Chi	X	χ	ch
Psi	Ψ	ψ	ps
Omega	Ω	ω	o (short)

Greek letters as abbreviations

α alpha — α-particle: a helium nucleus consisting of 2 protons and 2 neutrons and carrying a positive charge

α and ω — 'alpha and omega' – 'the beginning and the end'

β beta — β-particle: an electron emitted by a radioisotope during beta decay

γ gamma — γ-rays – a form of radioactivity similar to X-rays

η eta — efficiency: ratio of useful energy output of a machine to energy input

λ lambda — wavelenth

μ mu — 1. micro: submultiple prefix (10^{-6}); eg
μm: micrometre (one thousandth of a millimetre)
μs: microsecond (one millionth of a second)

2. permeability

π pi — mathematics constant: ratio of circumference of circle to diameter (value = 3.141 592 653 589 79 . . .)

ρ rho — 1. density

2. resistivity

Σ sigma — summation

σ sigma — standard deviation

ψ psi — electric flux

Ω omega — 1. ohm: unit of electric resistance

2. 'the end' (sometimes used to indicate last page of document)

Health bodies

National and general

ACHCEW	Association of Community Health Councils of England and Wales
CSA	Central Services Agency (for Northern Ireland)
CSASHS	Common Services Agency for the Scottish Health Service
DHA	district health authority (but word 'district' usually omitted from name of individual authority)
FPS	family practitioner services
HCHS	hospital and community health services
HEA	Health Education Authority (formerly HEC: Health Education Council)
MOEH	medical officer for environmental health
NAHA	National Association of Health Authorities in England and Wales
NHS	National Health Service
RCEP	Royal Commission on Environmental Pollution
RHA	regional health authority
WHCSA	Welsh Health Common Services Authority

Regional health authorities (England)

EARHA	East Anglian RHA
MRHA	Mersey RHA
NETRHA	North East Thames RHA
NRHA	Northern RHA
NWRHA	North Western RHA
NWTRHA	North West Thames RHA
ORHA	Oxford RHA
SETRHA	South East Thames RHA
SWRHA	South Western RHA
SWTRHA	South West Thames RHA
TRHA	Trent RHA
WMRHA	West Midlands RHA
WRHA	Wessex RHA
YRHA	Yorkshire RHA

Health boards (Scotland)

AAHB	Ayrshire and Arran HB
ACHB	Argyll and Clyde HB
BHB	Borders HB
DGHB	Dumfries and Galloway HB
FHB	Fife HB
FVHB	Forth Valley HB
GGHB	Greater Glasgow HB
GHB	Grampian HB
HHB	Highland HB
LHB	Lanarkshire HB
LHB	Lothian HB
OHB	Orkney HB
SHB	Shetland HB
THB	Tayside HB
WIHB	Western Isles HB

Health and social services boards (Northern Ireland)

EHSSB	Eastern HSSB
NHSSB	Northern HSSB
SHSSB	Southern HSSB
WHSSB	Western HSSB

Law reports

Abbreviations vary slightly in different sources, but this list should be sufficient for identifying the reports referred to.

AC	Appeal Cases (House of Lords and Privy Council decisions in The Law Reports)		JPEL	Journal of Planning and Environment Law
ALJR	Australian Law Journal Reports		KB	King's Bench Division (The Law Reports)
All ER	All England Law Reports (1936-present)			
All ER Rep	All England Law Reports Reprint (1558–1935)		LGR	Local Government Reports
			LJCP	Law Journal Common Pleas
ATC	Annotated Tax Cases		LJKB	Law Journal King's Bench
			LJQB	Law Journal Queen's Bench
BLR	Building Law Reports		Lloyd's Rep	Lloyds Law Reports (1951-present)
BLR	Business Law Review		LR	The Law Reports (1865-present)
			LT	Law Times (1859–1947)
CA	Court of Appeal			
C&P	Carrington and Payne (1823–41)		NLJ	New Law Journal
Ch, ChD	Chancery Division (The Law Reports)		NZLR	New Zealand Law Reports
CILL	Construction Industry Law Letter			
CLD	Construction Law Digest		P&CR	Planning and Compensation Reports
CLY	Current Law Yearbook		PC	Privy Council
CMLR	Common Market Law Reports (1962-present)		PLB	Property Law Bulletin
			PLR	Estates Gazette Planning Law Reports
Con LR	Construction Law Reports			
			QB	Queen's Bench Division (The Law Reports)
DE G M & G	DE Gex MacNaghten & Gordon			
EG	Estates Gazette		RA	Rating Appeals
EGCS	Estates Gazette Case Summaries		R&IT	Rating and Income Tax (1924–60)
EGD	Estates Gazette Digest of Cases (1902–84)		RRC	Ryde's Rating Cases
			RVR	Rating and Valuation Reporter
EGLR	Estates Gazette Law Reports (1985-present)			
			SC	Session Cases (Scotland) (1821-present)
Eq	Equity			
ER	English Reports		SJ	Solicitor's Journal (1857-present)
Ex	Exchequer		SLCR	Scottish Land Court Reports
Exch	Exchequer Reports		SLT	Scots Law Times
			STC	Simon's Tax Cases
FSR	Fleet Street Reports			
			Taunt	Taunton Reports
Giff	Gifford		TC	Tax Cases (1875-present)
			TLR	Times Law Reports (1884–1952; separate series from reports in The Times)
HL	House of Lords			
HLR	House of Lords Reports			
			VATTR	Value Added Tax Tribunal Reports
ICR	Industrial Cases/Court Reports			
IR	Irish Reports		WLR	Weekly Law Reports (1953-present)
			WN	Weekly Notes (1866–1952)
JP	Justice of the Peace Reports			

London postal districts

The districts in each postcode area are arranged alphabetically, not geographically, which is why the numbers of adjoining districts appear unrelated. This list explains the system.

E1	**EASTERN** Head District (Whitechapel)		NW1	**NORTH WESTERN** Head District (Regents Park)
E2	Bethnal Green		NW2	Cricklewood
E3	Bow		NW3	Hampstead
E4	Chingford		NW4	Hendon
E5	Clapton		NW5	Kentish Town
E6	East Ham		NW6	Kilburn
E7	Forest Gate		NW7	Mill Hill
E8	Hackney		NW8	St John's Wood
E9	Homerton		NW9	The Hyde
E10	Leyton		NW10	Willesden
E11	Leytonstone			
E12	Manor Park		NW11	Golders Green
E13	Plaistow			
E14	Poplar			
E15	Stratford			
E16	Victoria Docks and North Woolwich			
E17	Walthamstow		SE1	**SOUTH EASTERN** Head District (Southwark)
E18	Woodford and South Woodford		SE2	Abbey Wood
			SE3	Blackheath
EC1	**EASTERN CENTRAL** Head District (Clerkenwell)		SE4	Brockley
EC2	Eastern Central Head District (Moorgate)		SE5	Camberwell
EC3	Eastern Central Head District (Fenchurch Street)		SE6	Catford
			SE7	Charlton
EC4	Eastern Central Head District (St Paul's)		SE8	Deptford
			SE9	Eltham
N1	**NORTHERN** Head District (Islington and Hoxton)		SE10	Greenwich
			SE11	Kennington
N2	East Finchley		SE12	Lee
N3	Finchley, Church End		SE13	Lewisham
N4	Finsbury Park		SE14	New Cross
N5	Highbury		SE15	Peckham
N6	Highgate		SE16	Rotherhithe
N7	Holloway		SE17	Walworth
N8	Hornsey		SE18	Woolwich
N9	Lower Edmonton			
N10	Muswell Hill		SE19	Norwood
N11	New Southgate			
N12	North Finchley			
N13	Palmer's Green		SE20	Anerley
N14	Southgate		SE21	Dulwich
N15	South Tottenham		SE22	East Dulwich
N16	Stoke Newington		SE23	Forest Hill
N17	Tottenham		SE24	Herne Hill
N18	Upper Edmonton		SE25	South Norwood
N19	Upper Holloway		SE26	Sydenham
N20	Whetstone		SE27	West Norwood
N21	Winchmore Hill			
N22	Wood Green		SE28	Thamesmead

SW1	**SOUTH WESTERN** Head District (Westminster)		W1	**WESTERN** Head District (Oxford Street)
SW2	Brixton		W2	Paddington Head District
SW3	Chelsea		W3	Acton
SW4	Clapham		W4	Chiswick
SW5	Earl's Court		W5	Ealing
SW6	Fulham		W6	Hammersmith
SW7	South Kensington		W7	Hanwell
SW8	South Lambeth		W8	Kensington
SW9	Stockwell		W9	Maida Hill
SW10	West Brompton		W10	North Kensington
			W11	Notting Hill
SW11	Battersea Head District		W12	Shepherd's Bush
SW12	Balham		W13	West Ealing
SW13	Barnes		W14	West Kensington
SW14	Mortlake			
SW15	Putney		WC1	**WESTERN CENTRAL** Head District (Bloomsbury)
SW16	Streatham		WC2	Western Central Head District (Strand)
SW17	Tooting			
SW18	Wandsworth			
SW19	Wimbledon			
SW20	West Wimbledon			

London telephone exchange codes

London telephone exchange codes and the district served by each. The exchange code must be preceded by the appropriate area code, 071- or 081-. These superseded the single area code 01- on 6 May 1990.

Some codes have not been allocated, while others are allocated to government departments, hospitals and other large users and not included in British Telecom's published list of codes. Ring 0800 800 873 with enquiries about codes not shown here. Some codes have been allocated to Mercury Communications Ltd (see end of list). These do not relate to particular areas. Ring 021-625 3010 with enquiries about Mercury numbers.

INNER LONDON: area code 071-

210 Westminster	250 Clerkenwell	321 Westminster
214 "	251 "	323 Bloomsbury
215 "	252 Bermondsey, Walworth	326 Brixton
217 "	and Stepney	328 Kilburn and Maida Vale
218 "	253 Clerkenwell	329 St Pauls
219 "	254 Kingsland Green	
	255 Bloomsbury	350 Battersea
	256 Moorgate	351 Chelsea
220 Monument	257 Covent Garden	352 "
221 Bayswater	258 Paddington	353 Fleet Street
222 Westminster	259 Belgravia	354 Canonbury
223 Battersea		355 Mayfair
225 South Kensington		356 City
226 Canonbury	260 Moorgate	357 Moorgate
227 Westminster	261 Southbank	358 Peckham and New Cross
228 Battersea	262 Paddington	359 Canonbury
229 Bayswater	263 Upper Holloway	
	265 City of London	370 Earls Court
	and Wapping	371 Parsons Green
230 Westminster	266 Lords	372 Maida Vale
231 Bermondsey	267 Kentish Town	373 Earls Court
232 "		374 Moorgate
233 Westminster		375 Bishopsgate
234 Southwark	270 Westminster	376 Chelsea
235 Belgravia	271 "	377 Bishopsgate
236 St Pauls	272 Upper Holloway	378 Southwark
237 Bermondsey	273 Westminster	379 Covent Garden
238 Millbank	274 Brixton	
239 Kings Cross	276 Whitehall	380 Euston
	278 Kings Cross	381 Fulham
	279 Whitehall	382 Moorgate
240 Covent Garden		383 Euston
241 Kingsland Green		384 Parsons Green
242 Holborn	280 Monument	385 Fulham
243 Bayswater	281 Upper Holloway	386 "
244 Earl's Court	283 Monument	387 Euston
245 Belgravia	284 Kentish Town	388 "
247 Bishopsgate	286 Lords and Maida Vale	389 Whitehall
248 St Pauls	289 "	
249 Kingsland Green		

London telephone exchange codes

INNER LONDON continued

401	Southbank	580	Bloomsbury	720	Nine Elms
402	Paddington	581	South Kensington	721	Westminster
403	Southwark	582	Vauxhall	722	St Johns Wood
404	Holborn	583	Fleet Street	723	Paddington
405	"	584	South Kensington	724	"
407	Southwark	585	Parsons Green	725	North Paddington
408	Mayfair	586	St Johns Wood	726	City
409	"	587	Vauxhall	727	Bayswater
		588	Moorgate	729	Shoreditch
		589	South Kensington		
430	Holborn			730	Sloane
431	Hampstead	600	City	731	Parsons Green
432	City	601	"	732	Peckham and New Cross
433	Hampstead	602	West Kensington	733	Brixton
434	Soho	603	"	734	Soho
435	Hampstead	605	"	735	Vauxhall
436	Howland	606	City	736	Fulham
437	Soho	607	Lower Holloway	737	Brixton
438	Covent Garden	608	Clerkenwell	738	Battersea
439	Soho	609	Lower Holloway	739	Shoreditch
473	East Albert Dock	620	Southbank	790	Stepney Green
474	Plaistow	621	Monument	791	"
	and Canning Town	622	Nine Elms	792	Bayswater
		623	Monument	793	Vauxhall
		624	Kilburn, Maida Vale and	794	Hampstead
480	City of London		South Hampstead	796	City
	and Wapping	625	Kilburn and Maida Vale	798	Pimlico
481	"	626	Monument	799	Westminster
482	Kentish Town	627	Nine Elms		
483	St Johns Wood	628	Moorgate	820	Vauxhall
485	Kentish Town	629	Mayfair	821	Millbank
486	Marylebone			822	Fleet Street
487	"	630	Pimlico	823	Sloane
488	City of London	631	Bloomsbury	824	"
	and Wapping	632	"	826	Moorgate
489	St Pauls	633	Southbank	828	Pimlico
		634	St Pauls	829	Waterloo
		635	Peckham and New Cross		
490	Clerkenwell	636	Bloomsbury	831	Holborn
491	Mayfair	637	"	832	Highbury
492	"	638	Moorgate	833	Kings Cross
493	"	639	Peckham and New Cross	834	Pimlico
494	Gerrard			835	Earls Court
495	Mayfair	700	Lower Holloway	836	Covent Garden
497	Covent Garden	701	Camberwell and Walworth	837	Kings Cross
498	Nine Elms	702	City of London	839	Whitehall
499	Mayfair		and Wapping		
		703	Camberwell and Walworth		
		704	Lower Holloway		
511	Plaistow	706	Paddington		
	and Canning Town	707	Walworth		
515	Poplar	708	Camberwell and Walworth		
		709	City of London		
538	Poplar		and Wapping		

INNER LONDON continued

920	Moorgate	930	Westminster	987	Poplar
921	Southbank	931	Fulham		
922	"	932	Pimlico		
923	Kingsland Green	933	"		
924	Battersea	934	Southbank		
925	Whitehall	935	Marylebone		
927	Bloomsbury	936	Holborn		
928	Southbank	937	Kensington		
929	Monument	938	"		

OUTER LONDON: area code 081-

200	Colindale	330	Worcester Park	440	Barnet
202	Hendon	332	Richmond	441	Hadley Green and Barnet
203	"	335	Worcester Park	443	Ponders End
204	Kingsbury	336	New Malden	444	Muswell Hill
205	Colindale	337	Worcester Park	445	North Finchley
206	Kingsbury			446	"
207	Elstree	340	Hornsey and Highgate	449	Barnet
208	Cricklewood	341	"		
209	Golders Green	343	Finchley	450	Cricklewood and Dollis Hill
		346	"	451	Willesden
290	Bromley	347	Hornsey and Highgate	452	Cricklewood and Dollis Hill
291	Forest Hill	348	"	453	Harlesden
293	Greenwich	349	Finchley	455	Golders Green
294	Eltham			456	Colindale
295	Chislehurst	360	Winchmore Hill	458	Golders Green
297	Lee Green	361	Southgate	459	Willesden
298	Bexleyheath	363	Enfield		
299	Dulwich and Camberwell	364	"	460	Bromley
		365	Muswell Hill and Tottenham	461	Catford and Bellingham
				462	Hayes (Kent)
300	Sidcup	366	Enfield	463	Lee Green
301	Bexleyheath	367	"	464	Bromley
302	Sidcup	368	Southgate	466	"
303	Bexleyheath			467	Chislehurst and Bickley
304	"	390	Surbiton	468	"
305	Greenwich	391	Chessington	469	Deptford
308	Sidcup	392	Mortlake		
309	"	393	Ewell	470	East Ham
		394	"	471	"
310	Thamesmead	397	Chessington	472	"
311	"	398	Thames Ditton	475	Upton Park
312	"	399	Surbiton	478	Ilford
313	Bromley				
314	Rushey Green	421	Hatch End	500	Hainault
316	Woolwich and Plumstead	422	South Harrow	501	"
		423	"	502	Loughton
317	"	424	Harrow	504	Woodford and Buckhurst Hill
318	Lewisham	427	"	505	"
319	Woolwich, Eltham and Greenwich	428	Hatch End	506	Woodford
		429	Pinner and Eastcote	507	Barking
				508	Loughton
				509	Walthamstow

141

OUTER LONDON continued

514 Ilford
517 Dagenham
518 Ilford
519 Stratford and Forest Gate

520 Walthamstow
521 "
523 Highams Park
524 Chingford
527 Highams Park
529 Chingford

530 Wanstead
531 Highams Park
533 Hackney
534 Stratford and Forest Gate
536 "
539 Leytonstone

540 Merton and South
    Wimbledon
541 Kingston
542 Merton and South
    Wimbledon
543 "
545 "
546 Kingston
547 "
549 "

550 Barkingside
    and Redbridge
551 "
552 East Ham
553 Ilford
554 "
555 Stratford and Forest Gate
556 Leytonstone
558 "

560 Isleworth and Brentford
561 Hayes and Cranford
562 London Airport Heathrow
    and Harlington
563 Hammersmith
564 Skyport
566 Ealing
567 "
568 Isleworth
569 Hayes

570 Hounslow and Heston
571 Southall
572 Hounslow and Heston
573 Hayes and Cranford
574 Southall
575 Greenford
576 Shepherds Bush
577 Hounslow
578 Greenford
579 Ealing

590 Seven Kings
    and Goodmayes
591 Barking
592 Dagenham
593 "
594 Barking
595 Dagenham
597 Seven Kings
    and Goodmayes
598 "
599 "

640 Mitcham and Morden
641 Sutton and Cheam
642 Sutton and Belmont
643 "
644 Sutton and Cheam
645 Purley and Kenley
646 Mitcham and Morden
647 Wallington and Carshalton
648 Mitcham and Morden

650 Beckenham
651 Sanderstead and Selsdon
653 Norwood
654 Addiscombe and South
    Norwood
655 "
656 "
657 Sanderstead and Selsdon
658 Beckenham
659 Sydenham and Penge

660 Purley and Kenley
661 Sutton and Belmont
663 Beckenham
664 Streatham
666 Croydon
668 Purley and Kenley
669 Wallington and Carshalton

670 Gipsy Hill
    and West Norwood
671 Tulse Hill
    and Brixton Hill
672 Tooting and Balham
673 South Clapham
674 Tulse Hill and Brixton Hill
675 Balham
676 Sydenham
677 Streatham
679 Norbury

680 Croydon
681 "
682 Tooting and Balham
683 Thornton Heath
684 "
685 Mitcham and Morden
686 Croydon
687 Mitcham and Morden
688 Croydon
689 Thornton Heath

690 Catford
691 Deptford
692 "
693 Dulwich and Camberwell
694 Deptford
695 Catford
697 Catford and Bellingham
698 "
699 Forest Hill

740 Shepherds Bush
741 Hammersmith
742 Chiswick
743 Shepherds Bush
744 Twickenham
745 London Airport Heathrow
    and Harlington
746 Hammersmith
747 Chiswick
748 Hammersmith
749 Shepherds Bush

750 London Airport Heathrow
    and Harlington
751 Feltham and East Bedfont
752 Acton
755 Twickenham
756 Hayes and Cranford
758 Ealing
759 London Airport Heathrow
    and Harlington

142

OUTER LONDON continued

760	Croydon	861	Harrow	950	Bushey Heath
761	Gipsy Hill	863	"	951	Edgware
	and West Norwood	864	South Harrow	952	"
763	Purley and Kenley	866	Pinner and Eastcote	953	Elstree
764	Norbury	868	"	954	Stanmore
767	Tooting and Balham	869	South Harrow	958	Edgware
768	Norbury			959	Mill Hill
769	Streatham	870	Wandsworth		
		871	"	960	Kensal Green
770	Sutton and Belmont	874	"	961	Harlesden
771	Norwood	976	Mortlake		and Stonebridge Park
773	Wallington	877	Wandsworth	964	Kensal Green
776	West Wickham	878	Mortlake	965	Harlesden
777	"	879	Wimbledon	968	Kensal Green
778	Sydenham and Penge			969	"
		881	Wood Green		
780	Putney	882	Palmers Green		
783	Molesey	883	Muswell Hill	974	Chessington
785	Putney	884	Edmonton	977	Teddington
786	Ewell	885	Tottenham	979	East Molesey and Hampton
788	Putney	886	Palmers Green		
789	"	888	Wood Green		
		889	"	980	Bow and Mile End
800	Stamford Hill			981	"
801	Tottenham			983	East Poplar
802	Stamford Hill	890	Feltham and East Bedfont	985	Hackney
803	Edmonton	891	Twickenham	986	"
804	Ponders End	892	"	989	Wanstead
805	"	893	Feltham, Southall and		
806	Clapton		Twickenham		
807	Edmonton	894	Twickenham	991	Perivale, Alperton
808	Tottenham	897	London Airport Heathrow		and North Ealing
809	Stamford Hill		and Harlington	992	Acton
		898	Twickenham	993	Perivale, Alperton
840	Ealing				and North Ealing
841	Northolt and Yeading			994	Chiswick
842	"	900	Wembley	995	"
843	Southall	902	"	997	Perivale, Alperton
844	Feltham and East Bedfont	903	"		and North Ealing
845	Northolt and Yeading	904	North Wembley	998	"
846	Hammersmith	906	Mill Hill		
847	Isleworth and Brentford	907	Kenton		
848	Hayes and Cranford	908	North Wembley		
		909	Kenton		
850	Eltham				
851	Mottingham and Grove Park	940	Richmond	**MERCURY**	
852	Lewisham	941	East Molesey		
853	Greenwich		and Hampton	315	872
854	Woolwich and Plumstead	942	New Malden	334	873
855	"	943	Teddington	528	901
856	Woolwich, Eltham and	944	Wimbledon	548	945
	Greenwich	946	"	782	956
857	Mottingham and Grove Park	947	"	784	962
958	Greenwich	948	Richmond	860	975
859	Eltham	949	New Malden	867	982

Morse code

Hardly abbreviations, but definitely a code – in fact, a special kind of binary code. The original code was devised by Samuel Morse in 1837, but a simpler and more precise International Morse Code, given here, was agreed in 1851.

ALPHABET (1–4 digits)

Alphabetical order		Code order	
• —	A	•	E
— • • •	B	• •	I
— • — •	C	• • •	S
— • •	D	• • • •	H
•	E	• • • —	V
• • — •	F	• • —	U
— — •	G	• • — •	F
• • • •	H	• —	A
• •	I	• — •	R
• — — —	J	• — • •	L
— • —	K	• — —	W
• — • •	L	• — — •	P
— —	M	• — — —	J
— •	N	—	T
— — —	O	— •	N
• — — •	P	— • •	D
— — • —	Q	— • • •	B
• — •	R	— • • —	X
• • •	S	— • —	K
—	T	— • — •	C
• • —	U	— • — —	Y
• • • —	V	— —	M
• — —	W	— — •	G
— • • —	X	— — • •	Z
— • — —	Y	— — • —	Q
— — • •	Z	— — —	O

NUMERALS (5 digits)

• — — — —	1
• • — — —	2
• • • — —	3
• • • • —	4
• • • • •	5
— • • • •	6
— — • • •	7
— — — • •	8
— — — — •	9
— — — — —	0

PUNCTUATION (mainly 6 digits)

• — — — — •	apostrophe
— — — • • •	colon
— — • • — —	comma
— • • — •	fraction bar
• — • — • —	full stop
— • • • • —	hyphen
— • — — • —	parenthesis
• • — — • •	query
• — • • — •	quotation marks
• • • • • •	error

Multiples and submultiples

A = multiplier
B = prefix
C = symbol

A	B	C
10^{18}	exa	E
10^{15}	peta	P
10^{12}	tera	T
10^{9}	giga	G
10^{6}	mega	M
10^{3}	kilo	k
10^{2}	hecto	h
10^{1}	deca	da
10^{-1}	deci	d
10^{-2}	centi	c
10^{-3}	milli	m
10^{-6}	micro	μ
10^{-9}	nano	n
10^{-12}	pico	p
10^{-15}	femto	f
10^{-18}	atto	a

2FE

Phonetic alphabet

The phonetic alphabet was developed to meet the need for clarity in signalling. From the simple Ack Emma in use at the beginning of the century many more sophisticated variations evolved during the next fifty years. This International Phonetic Alphabet was officially approved in 1956.

A	ALFA
B	BRAVO
C	CHARLIE
D	DELTA
E	ECHO
F	FOXTROT
G	GOLF
H	HOTEL
I	INDIA
J	JULIET
K	KILO
L	LIMA
M	MIKE
N	NOVEMBER
O	OSCAR
P	PAPA
Q	QUEBEC
R	ROMEO
S	SIERRA
T	TANGO
U	UNIFORM
V	VICTOR
W	WHISKEY
X	X-RAY
Y	YANKEE
Z	ZULU

Plastics and rubbers

This highly technical field rivals computers for the production of abbreviations to bemuse specifiers and users. This list will help to identify and distinguish between them, but does not attempt to explain the chemistry. Both common names and chemical names or descriptions are given. Rubbers are identified as such; the rest are plastics. For further details of classification and terminology refer to BS 3502: Parts 1 and 3.

ABR	acrylate-butadiene rubber
ABS	acrylonitrile butadiene styrene copolymer
ACM	copolymer of ethylacrylate or other acrylate and a small amount of a monomer which facilitates vulcanisation (rubber)
AFMU	terpolymer of tetrafluoroethylene-tri-fluoronitrosomethane and nitrosoperfluorobutyric acid (rubber)
ANM	copolymer of ethylacrylate or other acrylate and acrylonitrile (rubber)
AR	acrylic rubber
AU	polyester rubber
BIIR	bromo-isobutene-isoprene (rubber)
BR	butadiene rubber
CA	acetate, cellulose acetate
CAB	butyrate, cellulose acetate butyrate
CAP	cellulose acetate propionate
CFM	polychlorotrifluoroethylene (rubber) (same as PCTFE)
CIIR	chloro-isobutene-isoprene (rubber)
CM	chloropolyethylene (rubber)
CN	celluloid, nitrate, cellulose nitrate
CO	polychloromethyloxiran (epichlorohydrin elastomer) (rubber)
CPE	chlorinated polyethylene
CPVC	post-chlorinated PVC
CR	chloroprene rubber, neoprene
CS	casein
CSM	chlorosulphonylpolyethylene, chlorosulphonated polyethylene, "Hypalon" (rubber)
CTA	triacetate, cellulose triacetate
DAP	as PDAP

ECO	ethylene oxide (oxiran) and chloromethlyoxiran (epichlorohydrin copolymer) (rubber)
EP	epoxy, epoxide resin
E/P	ethylene propylene
EPDM	ethylene propylene diene terpolymer; terpolymer of ethylene, propylene and a diene with the residual unsaturated portion of the diene in the side chain (rubber)
EPM	ethylene-propylene copolymer (rubber)
EPS	expanded polystyrene
EU	polyether rubber
EVA	as EVAC
EVAC	ethylene vinyl acetate copolymer
FEP	fluorinated ethylene propylene, perfluoroethylene propylene
FPM	rubber having fluoro and fluoroalkyl substituent groups on the polymer chain
FRP	as FRTP
FRTP	(fibre) reinforced thermoplastic
GPO	copolymer of propylene oxide and allyl glycidyl ether (rubber)
GRP	glass (fibre) reinforced plastic or polyester based on a thermosetting resin
HDPE	high density polyethylene
HMWPE	high molecular weight polyethylene
IIR	isobutene-isoprene rubber, polyisobutylene/isoprene, butyl rubber
IM	polyisobutene (rubber)
IR	isoprene rubber (synthetic) (cf NR)
LDPE	low density polyethylene
LLDPE	linear low density polyethylene

MF	melamine, melamine formaldehyde		POM	acetal, polyoxymethylene, polyformaldehyde (a polyacetal)
MFQ	silicone rubber having methyl and fluorine substituent groups on the polymer chain		PP	polypropylene, copolymer in which propylene is the main constituent
MPF	melamine phenol formaldehyde		PPO	as PPOX
MPQ	silicone rubber having methyl and phenyl substituent groups on the polymer chain		PPOX	polyphenylene oxide
			PS	polystyrene, toughened polystyrene, modified polystyrene, styrene
MPVQ	silicone rubber having methyl, phenyl and vinyl substituent groups on the polymer chain		PSBR	pyridine-styrene-butadiene rubber
MQ	silicone rubber having only methyl substituent groups on the polymer chain; eg dimethyl polysiloxane		PTFCE	polytrifluorochloroethylene
			PTFE	polytetrafluoroethylene, "Teflon"
			PU	as PUR
			PUR	urethane, polyurethane
MuPVC	modified unplasticised polyvinyl chloride		PVA	as PVAC or PVAL
			PVAC	polyvinyl acetate
MVQ	silicone rubber having methyl and vinyl substituent groups on the polymer chain		PVAL	polyvinyl alcohol
			PVC	vinyl, polyvinyl chloride, copolymer in which vinyl chloride is the main constituent
NBR	nitrile-butadiene rubber		PVDC	polyvinylidene chloride
NCR	nitrile-chloroprene rubber		PVDF	polyvinylidene fluoride
NIR	nitrile-isoprene rubber		PVF	polyvinyl fluoride
NR	natural rubber, isoprene rubber (natural) (cf IR)		RP	reinforced plastics
PA	nylon, polyamide		SAN	styrene acrylonitrile copolymer
PB	polybutene 1		SBR	styrene-butudiene rubber
PBR	pyridine-butadiene rubber		SCR	styrene-chloroprene rubber
PBT	as PBTP		SI	silicone, substituted polysiloxane (plastics)
PBTP	polybutylene terephthalate			
PC	polycarbonate		Si	silicone rubber
PCTFE	polychlorotrifluoroethylene (rubber) (same as CFM)		SIR	styrene-isoprene rubber
PDAP	polydiallyl phthalate		TPS	toughened polystyrene
PDCB	paradichlorobenzene		TR	thio rubber, polysulphide rubber
PE	polyethylene, "Polythene"			
PET	as PETP		UF	urea, urea-formaldehyde
PETP	polyester, polyethylene terephthalate		UP	polyester, unsaturated polyester
			uPVC	unplasticized polyvinyl chloride
PF	phenolic, phenol-formaldehyde			
PIB	polyisobutylene		XLPE	cross-linked polyethylene
PMMA	polymethyl methacrylate polymer		XNBR	carboxylic-nitrile-butadiene (rubber)
PMP	poly 4-methyl pentene-1, methyl pentene		XSBR	carboxylic-styrene-butadiene (rubber)

Postcodes

Introduced in the early 1970s, postcodes are now well established. In addition to their role in the mechanisation of the sorting of mail they have many business uses, such as the planning of marketing activities and the organisation of information in databases.

AB Aberdeen
AL St Albans, Hertfordshire

B   Birmingham
BA Bath
BB Blackburn
BD Bradford, West Yorkshire
BH Bournemouth
BL Bolton
BN Brighton
BR Bromley
BS Bristol
BT Belfast

CA Carlisle
CB Cambridge
CF Cardiff
CH Chester
CM Chelmsford
CO Colchester
CR Croydon
CT Canterbury, Kent
CV Coventry
CW Crewe

DA Dartford
DD Dundee
DE Derby
DG Dumfries
DH Durham
DL Darlington, Co Durham
DN Doncaster, South Yorkshire
DT Dorchester, Dorset
DY Dudley, West Midlands

E   London Eastern
EC London Eastern Central
EH Edinburgh
EN Enfield, Middlesex
EX Exeter

FK Falkirk
FY Blackpool

G   Glasgow
GL Gloucester
GU Guildford, Surrey

HA Harrow, Middlesex
HD Huddersfield
HG Harrogate, North Yorkshire
HP Hemel Hempstead, Hertfordshire
HR Hereford
HU Hull
HX Halifax, West Yorkshire

IG Ilford, Essex
IP Ipswich
IV Inverness

KA Kilmarnock, Ayrshire
KT Kingston-upon-Thames, Surrey
KW Kirkwall, Orkney
KY Kirkcaldy, Fife

L   Liverpool
LA Lancaster
LD Llandrindod Wells, Powys
LE Leicester
LL Llandudno, Gwynedd
LN Lincoln
LS Leeds
LU Luton

M   Manchester
ME Medway
MK Milton Keynes
ML Motherwell, Lanarkshire

N   London Northern
NE Newcastle-upon-Tyne
NG Nottingham
NN Northampton
NP Newport, Gwent
NR Norwich
NW London North Western

OL Oldham
OX Oxford

PA Paisley, Renfrewshire
PE Peterborough
PH Perth
PL Plymouth
PO Portsmouth
PR Preston

RG Reading
RH Redhill
RM Romford

S   Sheffield
SA Swansea
SE London South Eastern
SG Stevenage, Hertfordshire
SK Stockport, Cheshire
SL Slough
SM Sutton, Surrey
SN Swindon

SO Southampton
SP Salisbury
SR Sunderland
SS Southend-on-Sea
ST Stoke-on-Trent
SW London South Western
SY Shrewsbury

TA Taunton, Somerset
TD Galashiels, Selkirkshire
TF Telford, Salop
TN Tonbridge, Kent
TQ Torquay
TR Truro, Cornwall
TS Cleveland
TW Twickenham

UB Southall, Middlesex

W   London Western
WA Warrington
WC London Western Central
WD Watford
WF Wakefield, West Yorkshire
WN Wigan, Lancashire
WR Worcester
WS Walsall
WV Wolverhampton

YO York

ZE Lerwick, Shetland

The Isle of Man and the Channel Islands are not postcoded because they have their own postal authorities.

Professional and academic qualifications

These are some of the qualifications to be found amongst construction industry professionals.

ACA	Associate, Institute of Chartered Accountants (England and Wales)
ACIArb	Associate, Chartered Institute of Arbitrators
AFRAeS	Associate Fellow, Royal Aeronautical Society
AIA	Associate, Institute of Actuaries
AIArb	Associate, Institute of Arbitrators
ALI	Associate, The Landscape Institute
AMICE	Associate Member, Institution of Civil Engineers
AMIEE	Associate Member, Institution of Electrical Engineers
AMIHVE	Associate Member, Institute of Heating and Ventilating Engineers
AMIMunE	Associate Member, Institution of Municipal Engineers
AMIStructE	Associate Member, Institution of Structural Engineers
ARA	Associate, Royal Academy
ARCA	Associate, Royal College of Art
ARCS	Associate, Royal College of Science
ARIBA	Associate, Royal Institute of British Architects (pre-1971)
ARICS	Associate, Royal Institution of Chartered Surveyors
ARSA	Associate, Royal Scottish Academy
ARSH	Associate, Royal Society of Health
ARWA	Associate, Royal West of England Academy
BArch	Bachelor of Architecture
BSc	Bachelor of Science
CEng	Chartered Engineer
DA	Diploma in Architecture
DesRCA	Designer, Royal College of Art
DipArch, DiplArch	Diploma in Architecture
DipCD	Diploma in Civic Design
DipCons	Diploma in Conservation
DipTP, DiplTP	Diploma in Town Planning
DistTP	Distinction in Town Planning (RIBA)

FCIArb	Fellow, Chartered Institute of Arbitrators
FCIOB	Fellow, Chartered Institute of Building
FCSD	Fellow, Chartered Society of Designers
FIOA	Fellow, Institute of Acoustics
FLAS	Fellow, Land Agents Society
FLI	Fellow, The Landscape Institute
FRIBA	Fellow, Royal Institute of British Architects (pre-1971)
FRICS	Fellow, Royal Institution of Chartered Surveyors
FRS	Fellow, Royal Society
FRSA	Fellow. Royal Society of Arts
FRSE	Fellow, Royal Society Edinburgh
FRTPI	Fellow, Royal Town Planning Institute
FSA	Fellow. Society of Antiquaries
FSAI	Fellow, Society of Architectural Illustrators
LRIBA	Licentiate, Royal Institute of British Architects (pre-1971)
MBIAT	Member, British Institute of Architectural Technicians
MBIM	Member, British Institute of Management
MCD	Master of Civic Design
MCIOB	Member, Chartered Institute of Building
MCSD	Member, Chartered Society of Designers
MICE	Member, Institute of Civil Engineers
MIEE	Member, Institution of Electrical Engineers
MIERE	Member, Institution of Electronic and Radio Engineers
MIMechE	Member, Institution of Mechanical Engineers
MIMunE	Member, Institution of Municipal Engineers
MInstP	Member, Institute of Physics
MIStructE	Member, Institution of Structural Engineers
MRTPI	Member, Royal Town Planning Institute

MSIAD	Member, Society of Industrial Artists and Designers (now MCSD)	RSA	Royal Scottish Academy
		RSE	Royal Society of Edinburgh
		RWA	Member, Royal West of England Academy
RA	Royal Academician		
RDI	Distinction of Royal Design for Industry	SADG	Société des Architectes Diplômés par le Gouvernement
RegArch	Registered Architect		
RHA	Royal Hibernian Academy	WS	Writer to the Signet
RIBA	Member, Royal Institute of British Architects		

NRMNRABR

Roman numerals

Although cumbersome, Roman numerals are still in wide use – usually where a special graphic effect is required. Letters may be in upper or lower case. 1990 = MCMXC.

Alphabetical order

C	100
D	500
I	1
L	50
M	1000
$\overline{\text{M}}$	1 000 000
V	5
$\overline{\text{V}}$	5000
X	10

Numerical order

I	1
V	5
X	10
L	50
C	100
D	500
M	1000
$\overline{\text{V}}$	5000
$\overline{\text{M}}$	1 000 000

Standards organisations

Organisations involved with the making of standards, together with research and information bodies with related functions.

INTERNATIONAL

Worldwide

CEE	International Commission on Rules for the Approval of Electrical Equipment
CGPM	Conférence Générale des Poids et Mesures (General Conference on Weights and Measures)
CIE	Commission International de l'Eclairage (International Commission for Illumination – ICI)
CIPM	Commission International des Poids et Mesures
CISPR	International Special Committee on Radio Interference
FID	Fédération Internationale d'Information et de Documentation
IEC	International Electrotechnical Commission (CEI) (electrotechnical counterpart of ISO)
IFAN	International Federation for the Application of Standards
ISCA	International Standards Steering Committee for Consumer Affairs
ISO	International Organisation for Standardisation

	CASCO	ISO Committee on Conformity Assessment
	CERTICO	ISO Committee on Certification
	DEVCO	ISO Development Committee
	EXCO	ISO Executive Committee
	INFCO	ISO Standing Committee for the Study of Scientific and Technical Information on Standardisation
	PLACO	ISO Planning Committee
	STACO	ISO Standing Committee for the Study of Principles of Standardisation

UICB	Union Internationale des Centres du Batiment (International Union of Building Centres)

Europe

AECMA	Association Européenne des Constructeurs de Matériel Aerospatiel
CEEC	Construction Economics European Committee, or European Committee of Construction Economists
CEN	European Committee for Standardisation

	CENCER	CEN's certification body
	ECISS	European Committee for Iron and Steel Standardisation

CENELEC	European Committee for Electrotechnical Standardisation (electrotechnical counterpart of CEN)

	CECC	CENELEC Electronic Components Committee

CEPT	Conference Européenne des Administrations des Postes et Telecoms (European Posts and Telecommunications Conference)

	ETSI	European Telecommunications Standards Institute

ECHO	European Commission Host Organisation (computers)
JESI	Joint European Standards Institution (CEN/CENELEC)

Documentation
"CE"   CE mark, showing compliance of product with applicable essential
         requirements
EC   Eurocode
EN   European standard (Euronorm)
ENV   European prestandard
ESR   essential safety requirements
ETA   European technical approval
ETS   European technical specification
HD   harmonisation document
ID   interpretative document

Other

ABCA   Standards bodies of America, Britain, Canada and Australia
ARSO   African Regional Organisation for Standardisation
ASAC   Asian Standards Advisory Committee
ASMO   Arab Organisation for Standardisation and metrology
CMEA   Council for Mutual Economic Assistance
COPANT   Pan American Standards Commission
CSS   Commonwealth Standards Conference
PASC   Pacific Area Standards Congress
Tripartite Committee
         Governments and standards bodies of UK, France and Germany

NATIONAL

Europe

AENOR   Asociación Español de Normalización y Certificación (Spanish Standards
         Association)
AFF   An Foras Forbatha (National Institute for Physical Planning and
         Construction – Ireland)
AFNOR   Association Française de Normalisation (French Standards Association)
BAM   Bundesanstalt für Materialforschung und -prüfing (West Germany)
BC   Bouwcentrum (Building Centre – Netherlands)
BC   Byggecentrum (Building Centre – Denmark)
BSA   Byggeriets Studiearkiv (National Centre for Building Documentation –
         Denmark)
BSI   British Standards Institution
CES   Centro Edile SpA (Building Centre – Italy)
CIE   Centro Italiano dell'Edilivia (Italian Building Station)
CNR   Consiglio Nazionale delle Ricerche (National Research Centre – Italy)
CSTB   Centre Scientifique et Technique du Batiment (Scientific and Technical
         Building Centre – France)
CSTC   Centre Scientifique et Technique de la Construction (Building Research
         Centre – France)
DIN   DIN Deutsches Institut für Normung (German Institute for Standardisation)
DS   Dansk Standardiseringsraad (Danish Standards Organisation)
ELOT   Hellenic Organisation for Standardisation (Greece)
ENIU   Ente Nazionale Italiano di Unificazione (Italian National Standards
         Organisation)
IBN   Institut Belge de Normalisation (Belgian Institute for Standardisation)
IfBt   Institut für Bautechnik (West Germany)
IPQ   Instituto Portugès de Qualidade (Portugese Standards Institute)

155

Standards organisations

IRB	Informationszentrum RAUM und BAU der Fraunhofer Gesellschaft (Information Centre for Regional Planning and Building Construction of the Fraunhofer Society – West Germany)
NBD	Nederlandse Bouw-Dokumentatie BV (Dutch Building Documentation Centre)
NNI	Nederlandse Normalisatie Instituut (Dutch Standardisation Institution)
NSAI	National Standards Authority of Ireland
SBI	Statens Byggeforskningsinstitut (Danish Building Research Institute)
SBR	Stiching Bouwresearch (Building Research Foundation – Netherlands)
SGNBT	Subdirección General Normativa Básica y Tecnológica/MOPU (National Institute for Quality in Building – Spain)
TIB	Technische Informationsbibliothek (Library for Technical Information – West Germany)

Other

ANSI	American National Standards Institute
ASA	American Standards Association
CSA	Canadian Standards Association
JSA	Japanese Standards Association

Symbols

´	acute accent
&	ampersand ('and')
'	apostrophe
→	appropriate limit of
≃	approximately equal to
*	asterisk
@	at
\	backslash
∵	because
•	bullet
¢	cent
^	circumflex accent
:	colon
,	comma
©	copyright
{ }	curly braces, enveloping brackets
†	dagger
.	decimal point
°	degree (angle: $1° = \pi/180$ rad)
°	degree (temperature)
⌀	diameter
"	ditto
÷	divided by
$	dollar
" "	double quotes
. . .	ellipsis (omission, 'and so on')
=	equals
≡	equivalent to
!	exclamation mark
↑	exponentiation
$r!$	factorial r
'	foot
.	full stop
^{G} or ^{g}	grade, or gon (angle: $1^G = \pi/200$ rad, or one hundredth of a right angle)
`	grave accent
>	greater than
≥	greater than or equal to
#	hash, numbers (USA)
-	hyphen
"	inch
△	increment
∞	infinity
⋀	insert
∫	integration sign
¡	inverted exclamation mark
¿	inverted question mark

<	less than
≤	less than or equal to
−	minus
'	minute (angle: degree/60)
×	multiplied by (times)
≠	not equal to
∦	not parallel
r^n	nth power of r
$^n\sqrt{r}$	nth root of r
○	open circle
¶	paragraph sign
∥	parallel
( )	parentheses
%	per cent (hundred)
‰	per mille (thousand)
+	plus
±	plus or minus
£	pound
?	question mark
« »	quotes (French)
®	registered
"	second (angle: minute/60)
§	section
;	semi colon
' '	single quotes
/	slash, oblique
[ ]	square brackets
√	square root
Σ	summation
∴	therefore
~	tilde
™	trade mark
¨	umlaut
α	varies with
|	vertical bar
Ø	zero with slash

Unions

The construction industry embraces a wide range of professions, trades and specialities, and its members are represented by an equal variety of trade unions and associations. This list includes some of the main ones and some related organisations of interest.

AMU	Associated Mineworkers Union
APEX	Association of Professional, Executive, Clerical and Computer Staff
ASBSBSW	Amalgamated Society of Boilermakers, Shipwrights, Blacksmiths and Structural Workers
ASTMS	Association of Scientific, Technical and Managerial Staffs (now merged with TASS to form MSF)
AUAW	Amalgamated Union of Asphalt Workers
AUEW	Amalgamated Union of Engineering Workers
AUT	Association of University Teachers
CATU	Ceramic and Allied Trades Union
CCSU	Council of Civil Service Unions
COHSE	Confederation of Health Service Employees
CPSA	Civil and Public Services Association
CSEU	Confederation of Shipbuilding and Engineering Unions
CSU	Civil Service Union
EETPU	Electrical, Electronic, Telecommunications and Plumbing Union (aka EEPTU)
EMA	Engineers and Managers Association
EPEA	Electrical Power Engineers Association
ETUC	European Trade Union Confederation
ETUI	European Trade Union Institute
FBU	Fire Brigades Union
FTAT	Furniture, Timber and Allied Trades Union
FUMPO	Federated Union of Managerial and Professional Officers
GFTU	General Federation of Trade Unions
GMWU	General and Municipal Workers Union

ICFTU	International Confederation of Free Trade Unions
IPCS	Institution of Professional Civil Servants
ISTC	Iron and Steel Trades Confederation
JCLMTU	Joint Committee of Light Metal Trades Unions
MATSA	Managerial, Administrative, Technical and Supervisory Association (GMWU non-manual workers section)
MSF	Manufacturing Science Finance
NALGO	National and Local Government Officers Association
NATSOPA	National Society of Operative Printers, Graphical and Media Personnel
NATFHE	National Association of Teachers in Further and Higher Education
NCCC	National Craftsmen's Co-ordinating Committee (iron and steel industry)
NFFTU	National Federation of Furniture Trade Unions
NGA	National Graphical Association
NSMM	National Society of Metal Mechanics
NUAAW	National Union of Agricultural and Allied Workers
NUB	National Union of Blastfurnacemen, Ore Miners, Coke Workers and Kindred Trades
NUDAGMW	National Union of Domestic Appliances and General Metal Workers
NUJ	National Union of Journalists
NULMW	National Union of Lock and Metal Workers
NUM	National Union of Mineworkers
NUPE	National Union of Public Employees
NUSMCHDE	National Union of Sheet Metal Workers, Coppersmiths, Heating and Domestic Engineers

NUT	National Union of Teachers	TASS	Technical Administrative and Supervisory Section (AUEW) (now merged with ASTMS to form MSF)
NUWDAT	National Union of Wallcoverings Decorative and Allied Trades		
POEU	Post Office Engineering Union	TGWU	Transport and General Workers Union
SCALA	Society of Chief Architects of Local Authorities	TSSA	Transport Salaried Staffs Association
SCPS	Society of Civil and Public Servants	TUAC	Trade Union Advisory Committee (OECD)
SLADE	Society of Lithographic Artists, Designers, Engravers and Process Workers	TUC	Trades Union Congress
		TURU	Trade Union Research Unit
SOGAT	Society of Graphical and Allied Trades	UCATT	Union of Construction, Allied Trades and Technicians
STAMP	Supervisory, Technical, Administrative, Managerial and Professional (UCATT white-collar section)	UCW	Union of Communication Workers
		URTU	United Road Transport Union

United Nations

Since its formation in 1945 the United Nations has spawned an almost countless number of councils, commissions, committees and special bodies. This list gives just an indication of the organisational structure of the UN and a selection of some of the more significant organisations.

Secretariat
Secretary General = principal administrator

General Assembly (GA) – all members (159 at October 1988)
Main Committees
Other sessional committees
Political and security matters
Trust territory and colonial questions
Development
    CDUNRSE   Committee on the Development and Utilisation of New and Renewable Sources of Energy
    ICSTD   Intergovernmental Committee on Science and Technology for Development
Legal questions
Administrative and financial questions

Security Council (SC) – 15 members

Economic and Social Council (ECOSOC) – 54 members
Sessional Committees
Functional Commissions
    PC   Population Commission
    SC   Statistical Commission
Committees and subsidiary bodies
    CDP   Committee for Development Planning
    CHS   Commission on Human Settlements
    CNR   Committee on Natural Resources
Regional Commissions
    ECA   Economic Commission for Africa
    ECE   Economic Commission for Europe
    ECLAC   Economic Commission for Latin America and the Caribbean
    ESCAP   Economic and Social Commission for Asia and the Pacific
    ESCWA   Economic and Social Commission for Western Asia

International Court of Justice (ICJ) or World Court

United Nations training and research institutes
    INSTRAW   UN International Research and Training Institute for the Advancement of Women
    UFP   University for Peace
    UNITAR   UN Institute for Training and Research
    UNRISD   UN Research Institute for Social Development
    UNU   UN University

Specialised Agencies of the UN
    FAO   Food and Agriculture Organisation
    GATT   General Agreement on Tariffs and Trade
    IAEA   International Atomic Energy Authority

IBRD	International Bank for Reconstruction and Development (World Bank)
	MIGA Multilateral Investment Guarantee Agency
ICAO	International Civil Aviation Organisation
IDA	International Development Association
IFAD	International Fund for Agricultural Development
IFC	International Finance Corporation
ILO	International Labour Organisation
IMF	International Monetary Fund
IMO	International Maritime Organisation
ITU	International Telecommunication Union
UNESCO	UN Educational, Scientific and Cultural Organisation
UNIDO	UN Industrial Development Organisation
UPU	Universal Postal Union
WHO	World Health Organisation
WIPO	World Intellectual Property Organisation
WMO	World Meteorological Organisation
	MTN Main Telecommunication Network
	RMC regional meteorological centre
	WCAP World Climate Applications Programme
	WCDP World Climate Data Programme
	WCIP World Climate Impact Studies Programme
	WCP World Climate Programme
	WCRP World Climate Research Programme
	WMC world meteorological centre

Other United Nations bodies

ISBA	International Sea-Bed Authority
UNCHS	UN Centre for Human Settlements
UNCLOS	UN Conference on the Law of the Sea
UNCTAD	UN Conference on Trade and Development
UNDP	UN Development Programme
	RFNRE UN Revolving Fund for Natural Resources Exploration
	UNCDF UN Capital Development Fund
	UNFSTD UN Fund for Science and Technology for Development
UNDRO	UN Disaster Relief Organisation (Office of the UN Disaster Relief Co-ordinator)
UNEP	UN Environment Programme
	GEMS Global Environment Monitoring System
	GRID Global Resource Information Database
	IRPTC International Register of Potentially Toxic Chemicals
	IUCN International Union for the Conservation of Nature and Natural Resources
	PACD UN Plan of Action to Combat Desertification
UNFPA	UN Population Fund (formerly UN Fund for Population Activities – acronym retained)
UNICEF	UN Children's Fund

Units of measurement

QUANTITY	SI UNIT	SYMBOL AND DERIVATION
BASIC SI UNITS		
Length	metre	m
Time	second	s
Amount of substance	mole	mol
Mass	kilogram	kg
Electric current	ampere	A
Thermodynamic temperature	kelvin	k
Luminous intensity	candela	cd
ANGULAR MEASURE		
Plane angle	radian	rad
Solid angle	steradian	sr
DERIVED SI UNITS		
Frequency	hertz	$Hz = 1/s$
Force	newton	$N = kg\,m/s^2$
Pressure, stress	pascal	$Pa = N/m^2$
Work, energy, quantity of heat	joule	$J = Nm$
Power	watt	$W = J/s$
Electric charge	coulomb	$C = As$
Electric capacitance	farad	$F = C/V$
Electrical potential	volt	$V = W/A$
Electric resistance	ohm	$\Omega = V/A$
Electric conductance	siemens	$S = 1/\Omega$
Magnetic flux	weber	$Wb = Vs$
Magnetic flux density	tesla	$T = Wb/m^2$
Inductance	henry	$H = W/A$
Luminous flux	lumen	$lm = cd\,sr$
Illuminance	lux	$lx = lm/m^2$

Utilities

COAL

Department of Energy (DEn)

ACRDFP	Advisory Council on Research and Development for Fuel and Power
BCC	British Coal Corporation
DCCC	Domestic Coal Consumers Council

ELECTRICITY

National

CEGB	Central Electricity Generating Board (superseded by NP and PG for generation, NGC for transmission)
DES	Director of Electricity Supply (OER)
EAL	Electricity Association Limited
EC	Electricity Council (1958-1989. Partly superseded by EAL)
ECC	Electricity Consumers Council
ECRC	Electricity Council Research Centre
NE	Nuclear Electric
NGC	National Grid Company
NP	National Power (= National Power Company, NPC)
NSAC	Nuclear Safety Advisory Committee
OER	Office of Electricity Regulation
PG	PowerGen (= Power Generation Company, PGC)

Area electricity boards (EBs)

England and Wales
Now electricity distribution companies (EDCs)

EE	Eastern Electricity
EME	East Midlands Electricity
LEB	London Electricity Board
Manweb	Merseyside and North Wales Electricity Board (formerly Manchester . . .)
MEB	Midlands Electricity Board
NEEB	North Eastern Electricity Board
NORWEB	North Western Electricity Board
SEEBOARD	South Eastern Electricity Board
SWE	South Wales Electricity
SWEB	South Western Electricity Board
SE	Southern Electric
YE	Yorkshire Electricity

Scotland

NSHEB	North of Scotland Hydro-Electric Board
SSEB	South of Scotland Electricity Board

Northern Ireland

NIES	Northern Ireland Electricity Service

Electricity consultative councils (ECCs)

England and Wales
12 English and Welsh electricity board ECCs

Scotland

NSECC	North of Scotland ECC
SSECC	South of Scotland ECC

Northern Ireland

GCCNI	General Consumer Council for Northern Ireland

GAS

National

AGE	Area Gas Examiner (one for each of four areas)
BG	British Gas
CGE	Chief Gas Engineer (DEn)
GCC	Gas Consumers Council
Ofgas	Office of Gas Supply

British Gas regions

BG–E	Eastern
BG–EM	East Midlands
BG–N	Northern
BG–NE	North Eastern
BG–NT	North Thames
BG–NW	North Western
BG–S	Scottish
BG–S	Southern
BG–SE	South Eastern
BG–SW	South Western
BG–W	Wales
BG–WM	West Midlands

WATER

National

DGWS	Director General of Water Services
NRA	National Rivers Authority
OWS	Office of Water Services
WBAS	Water Byelaws Advisory Service
WRc	Water Research Centre

Regional water authorities (RWAs)

England and Wales
Public limited companies from 1989; former names in brackets where different.

AW	Anglian Water
NWG	Northumbrian Water Group (NW: Northumbrian Water)
NWWG	North West Water Group (NWWA: North West Water Authority)
ST	Severn Trent (STW: Severn-Trent Water)
SW	Southern Water (SWA: Southern Water Authority)
SWW	South West Water
TW	Thames Water (TWA: Thames Water Authority)
WW	Welsh Water (WWA: Welsh Water Authority)
WW	Wessex Water (WWA: Wessex Water Authority)
YW	Yorkshire Water
WAA	Water Authorities Association

Scotland
12 regional and islands councils, plus:

CSWDB	Central Scotland Water Development Board

Northern Ireland

WS	Water Service operated by Department of the Environment for Northern Ireland (DoENI) through:
WSED	WS Eastern Division
WSND	WS Northern Division
WSSD	WS Southern Division
WSWD	WS Western Division

River purification boards (RPBs)

Scotland

CRPB	Clyde RPB
FRPB	Forth RPB
HRPB	Highland RPB
NERPB	North-East RPB
SRPB	Solway RPB
TRPB	Tay RPB
TRPB	Tweed RPB

Statutory water companies (WCs)

England and Wales

BDWC	Bournemouth and District WC
BWC	Bristol WC
CVWC	Colne Valley WC
CWC	Cambridge WC
CWC	Chester WC
EAWC	East Anglian WC
ESWC	East Surrey WC
EWC	Eastbourne WC
EWC	Essex WC
EWWC	East Worcestershire WC
FDWC	Folkestone and District WC
HWC	Hartlepools WC
LVWC	Lee Valley WC
MKWC	Mid-Kent WC
MSWC	Mid Southern WC
MSWC	Mid-Sussex WC
NGWC	Newcastle and Gateshead WC
NSWC	North Surrey WC
PWC	Portsmouth WC
RWC	Rickmansworth WC
SDWC	Sutton District WC
SSSWC	Sunderland and South Shields WC
SSWC	South Staffordshire WC
THWC	Tendring Hundred WC
WEDWC	Wrexham and East Denbighshire WC
WHWC	West Hampshire WC
WKWC	West Kent WC
YWC	York WC
WCA	Water Companies Association

Part 3
Bibliography

Bibliography

BOOKS OF GENERAL ABBREVIATIONS

While this guide concentrates on abbreviations relating to or affecting the construction industry, it includes a number of more general ones to increase its usefulness as an everyday reference book. For those who need more comprehensive lists there are several available, of which the following is a selection. One or more of these should be found in any public reference library.

British initials and abbreviations
Ian Wilkes
Leonard, 3rd edition 1971

Cassells dictionary of abbreviations
J W Gurnett and C H J Kyte (compiler)
Cassell, 2nd edition 1972
The complete dictionary of abbreviations
Robert Schwartz
Harrap, 1955 (USA)
Cyclopaedia of initials and abbreviations
F Dubrez Fawcett
Business Publications, London, 1963

A dictionary of acronyms and abbreviations
Eric Pugh
Library Association, 5th revised edition 1987
A dictionary of graphical symbols
L J Robinson
F C Avis (London), 1972
The dictionary of initials: what they mean
Harriette Lewis
Paperfronts, Elliot Right Way Books, 1983

Everymans dictionary of abbreviations
J Paxton
J M Dent & Sons, 4th revised edition 1986

The international dictionary of graphic symbols
Joel Arnstein
Kogan Page, 1983

SOURCES OF FURTHER INFORMATION ON ORGANISATIONS AND TECHNICAL DATA

The guide explains what abbreviations stand for. It does not generally give further information such as what technical terms actually mean or what an organisation does and how to contact it. For this more detailed information refer to the many dictionaries, glossaries, directories and textbooks available, such as those listed below.

British standards
BS 3502:
  Schedule of common names and abbreviations for plastics and rubbers
  Part 1: 1978: *Principal commercial plastics*
  Part 3: 1978: *Rubbers and latices*
BS 5374: 1981:
  Specification for codes for the representation of names of countries
BS 6879: 1987:
  Specification for codes for the representation of names of counties and similar areas

1992 – an information pack for architects
  RIBA Market Research Unit, 1989

AJ information guide 1987
  Supplement to Architects' Journal 14.10.87
The architect's phonebook
  Marketing to Architects Ltd, 1988

Basic facts: computers
  Brian Sanways
  Collins Gem, Collins, London and Glasgow, 1983
Building contract dictionary
  Vincent Powell-Smith and David Chappell
  Architectural Press, 1985

CIRIA guide to European Community and international sources of construction information
  CIRIA Special Publication 60, 1989

The CIRIA UK construction information guide
  CIRIA
  E&FN Spon, 1989
Common arrangement of work sections for building works
  Building Project Information Committee, 1987
A concise dictionary of data processing and computer terms
  R G Anderson
  Macdonald and Evans, 2nd edition 1984
Concise encyclopedia of architectural practice
  David Chappell and Ray Cecil
  Legal Studies and Services, 1989
Croner's Europe
  Looseleaf with amendment service
  Croner, 1988

Dictionary of computing
  Ian Sinclair
  Collins, 1988
Dictionary of computing
  Valerie Illingworth (general editor)
  OUP, 3rd revised edition 1990
Dictionary of quantities and units
  J V Drazil
  Leonard Hill, 2nd edition 1972
A dictionary of scientific units
  H G Jerrard and D B McNeill
  Chapman and Hall, 5th edition 1986
Directory of official architecture and planning
  S Higgins (editor)
  Longman, 29th edition 1990

167

Directory of pressure groups and representative associations
Peter Shipley
Bowker, 1979

Europa world year book
Europa Publications, 1990

The glossary of property terms
Jones Lang Wootton (compilers)
Estates Gazette Ltd, 1989
The Guinness book of answers
Norris McWhirter (general editor)
Guinness Superlatives Ltd, 7th edition, 1989

Legal reminders for architects
Elizabeth Phillips and Meyricke Sergeantson
Architectural Press, 1988

Macmillan dictionary of building
Randall McMullan
Macmillan, 1988
Mozley and Whiteley's law dictionary
10th edition 1988
Municipal year book and public services directory
Municipal Publications Ltd, annual

New metric handbook
Patricia Tutt and David Adler (editors)
Architectural Press, 1979

Penguin dictionary of architecture
John Fleming, Hugh Honour and Nikolas Pevsner
Penguin Books, 3rd edition 1980

Penguin dictionary of building
John Scott
Penguin Books, 3rd edition 1984
Penguin dictionary of civil engineering
John Scott
Penguin Books, 3rd edition, 1980
The Penguin dictionary of microprocessors
Anthony Chandor
Penguin Books, 1981

The shorter forms of building contract
Hugh Clamp
Blackwell Scientific Publications, 2nd edition 1988
Specification 90
Alastair Blyth (editor)
MBC Architectural Press and Building Publications, 84th edition 1989

The trade union directory – a guide to all TUC unions
Jack Easton and Colin Gill
Pluto Press, 1981

The UK construction industry and the European community
Building magazine and the National Council of Building Material Producers, 2nd edition 1989

Which contract? – choosing the appropriate building contract
Hugh Clamp and Stanley Cox
RIBA Publications, 1989